Prim-Ed Publishing

WORKBOOK

Learn from Home WORKBOOK

English, Mathematics and Science Activities

Learn from Home – Workbook 2

Published by Prim-Ed Publishing 2020
Copyright© R.I.C. Publications® 2020

ISBN 978-1-912760-62-6

PR–8489

Titles available in this series:

Learn from Home–Workbook 1 – *1st Class/Year 1*
Learn from Home–Workbook 2 – *2nd Class/Year 2*
Learn from Home–Workbook 3 – *3rd Class/Year 3*
Learn from Home–Workbook 4 – *4th Class/Year 4*
Learn from Home–Workbook 5 – *5th Class/Year 5*
Learn from Home–Workbook 6 – *6th Class/Year 6*

Prim-Ed Publishing
Marshmeadows
New Ross
Co. Wexford
Y34 TA46
Ireland

Ireland: (051) 440075

UK: +44 (0) 20 3773 9630

Email: sales@prim-ed.com

Internet websites
In some cases, websites or specific URLs may be recommended. While these are checked and rechecked at the time of publication, the publisher has no control over any subsequent changes which may be made to webpages. It is *strongly* recommended that the class teacher checks *all* URLs before allowing pupils to access them.

CONTENTS PAGE

Week 1 .... **2**

Week 2 .... **28**

Week 3 .... **54**

Week 4 .... **80**

WEEK 1

ENGLISH

Comprehension – How Lightning Came to Earth 3–5
Comprehension – A Letter to a Brother 6–8
Grammar – Nouns 9
Grammar – Proper Nouns 10
Writing – Narrative, The Missing Cakes 11–13
Editing Skills – Make a Milkshake 14
Editing Skills – Bobby Pop 15
Editing Skills – The Story of Digestion 16

MATHEMATICS

Number – Odd and Even Numbers 17
Number – Skip Counting 18
Number – Addition Number Stories 19
Measurement – The Centimetre 20
Measurement – More Centimetres 21
Geometry – 2-D Shapes 22
Geometry – Drawing by Instruction 23

SCIENCE

Magnetism and Electricity – Magnets 24
Magnetism and Electricity – Electricity 25
Materials – Describing Objects 26
Materials – Grouping Objects 27

How Lightning came to Earth – 1

Text

Read the fantasy.

Long ago, there were only dragons on Earth. The sun always shone and dragon flames were always hot.

There were two clans of dragons—sea dragons and land dragons. The sea dragons ruled the seas, oceans and the land where they nested. The land dragons ruled the inland and mountains. The two clans argued about who owned the nesting land.

Eard, the king of the land dragons, lived in a cave with his son, Draca. In a cave near the sea, Flot, the king of the sea dragons, lived with his son, Wyrm. One day, near the nesting field, Draca and Wyrm met. They talked and played together and became close friends. The two clans still argued about the nesting land.

Finally, the dragons decided to end the feud. They chose one champion from each clan. The winner would claim the nesting land. Draca and Wyrm were chosen. They were very sad. They did not want to fight each other but they had to do what the kings said. Claws ripped. Flames flashed across the sky. Tails lashed.

From Heaven, Dryhten, the dragon god, watched sadly. The land and sea dragons were greedy and selfish. They would kill the friends. Thunder roared and the sky grew black. The champions fell to the ground. Sweat, blood and tears poured from their bodies.

'Look what you have done!' roared Dryhten. 'You almost killed something special. Draca and Wyrm are the only ones who know how to end the feud. Being friends and understanding each other is the way.'

The land and sea dragons felt ashamed. Dryhten was right. They had been greedy and selfish. They picked up Draca and Wyrm in their wings and took them home to look after them. The land and sea dragons agreed to share the nesting land.

From that day on, the sun did not shine every day. Sometimes grey clouds flashed with flames like the breath of dragons fighting. The flashes remind everyone not to be greedy and selfish. They remind us to be friends and to try to understand each other. The flashes became known as lightning.

My learning log	When I read this fantasy text, I could read:		
	________ all of it.	________ most of it.	________ parts of it.

How Lightning came to Earth – 2

Comprehension

1. Which event made the sea and land dragons decide to end the feud about the nesting land?

____

____

2. Which words in the text are often used to begin stories and tales?

____

3. Write words from the text for these meanings.

   (a) use or build a nest: n__________

   (b) a close group of interrelated families, especially in the Scottish Highlands: c__________

   (c) people surpassing all rivals in a sporting contest or other competition: ch__________

   (d) a long, bitter quarrel or dispute: f__________

4. Do you think either of the dragon kings knew their sons were friends?

   Yes No Why? __________

____

5. Do you think Draca and Wyrm were still friends after the battle?

   Yes No Why? __________

____

6. Write one thing about dragons you knew before reading the text.

____

7. Write words, a phrase or a sentence that you like from the text.

____

My learning log	While doing these activities:		
	I found Q ____ easy.	I found Q ____ tricky.	I found Q ____ fun.

How Lightning came to Earth – 3

1. Which word from the text is a homophone for each word below?

   (a) there ____________ (b) to ____________ (c) bee ____________

   (d) see ____________ (e) won ____________ (f) sun ____________

   (g) weigh ____________ (h) knot ____________

2. Circle the correct homophone in the sentences.

   (a) The children went for a walk in the **wood** / **would**.

   (b) Sam planted a **been** / **bean** in the garden.

   (c) Kara wanted to **right** / **write** an email.

   (d) Alex couldn't decide which trousers to **where / wear**.

3. (a) Write and read words with a long 'i' sound at the end, spelt with a 'y' like 'try'.

   cr____ fl____ dr____ repl____ Jul____

   (b) Find and write another word in the text with this ending. ____________

4. What suffix ends the word 'sadly'? ____________

5. Divide each word into syllables for easier reading.

   (a) champions ____________

   (b) ashamed ____________

   (c) dragon ____________

   (d) selfish ____________

   (e) sometimes ____________

   (f) mountains ____________

   (g) across ____________

My learning log	Write **Yes** or **No**. I know which homophone to use. ____________ I can read words ending with a long 'i' sound. ____________ I can divide some words into syllables. ____________

A Letter to a Brother – 1

Text

Read the letters.

Dear Brother,

Letter 1

Thank you for your letter. Unfortunately, it arrived too late. Having found my own perfect place, I chose sticks to build my home. Of course, sticks are much stronger than straw, but harder to bend and shape. I joined them together with twine and thought I had built the perfect home.

Then, the wolf came to call. That wolf sure has a set of lungs! He blew my sturdy home away! Nothing was left except a pile of broken twigs! I am writing to our oldest brother tonight to see if he is managing better. I hope he chooses the strongest material possible. He is always such a good planner. I am sure he will be very careful. But that wolf is a huge nuisance!

Your loving older brother

Dear Brother,

Letter 2

It has been some time now since Mother sent us out to seek our fortune. I am writing to give you some important information so you can learn from my mistakes.

I found the perfect place to build my home so I searched for the perfect material to make it. Straw was cheap, light, easy to find and easy to bend to shape. I could make my home very quickly.

After I had completed it, the wolf came to visit. In a huff and a puff, my beautiful home was blown away and I was homeless. Straw was not a good choice after all! Please use a stronger material to build your home. Your life depends on it!

Your loving younger brother

Dear Brothers,

Letter 3

After slaving hard for many weeks, my beautiful brick home is completed. It is strong and weatherproof. It was worth all the work! Please come and visit soon. I've made a tasty wolf stew.

Your loving older (and wiser) brother

My learning log	When I read these letters, I could read:		
	_________ all of them.	_________ most of them.	_________ parts of them.

A Letter to a Brother – 2

Comprehension

1. Which brother wrote Letter 2? Underline the correct answer.

   (a) youngest brother (b) oldest brother (c) middle brother

2. Tick the correct statements. These letters:

   (a) tell a story. ☐

   (b) give information about materials. ☐

   (c) try to persuade the reader about a point of view. ☐

3. Which language feature is included in all three letters? Circle the answers.

   (a) a greeting (b) a farewell (c) steps

   (d) a list of ingredients (e) Once upon a time …

   (f) … and they lived happily ever after

4. Write a meaning for each word.

   (a) fortune ______________________

   (b) twine ______________________

   (c) nuisance ______________________

   (d) weatherproof ______________________

5. How was the oldest brother able to make wolf stew?

   ____

6. Do you think the two younger pigs will visit their older brother?

   Yes No Why? ______________________

   ____

7. Write a question about something in the text that needed more information.

   ____

8. What fairy tale are the letters about? ______________________

My learning log	While doing these activities:		
	I found Q _____ easy.	I found Q _____ tricky.	I found Q _____ fun.

A Letter to a Brother – 3

1. (a) Find and write a word in Letter 1 that starts with 'wr'. ____________

   (b) Underline the words that start with 'wr'.

week	**write**	**worth**	**work**	**wriggle**	**wrestle**
wrong	**wrap**	**wolf**	**wreck**	**wrist**	**war**

2. (a) Find and write two words in Letter 3 that start with 'wor'.

   ____________ ____________

   (b) Complete these words with the same 'or' sound.

   w________d w________m w________ld

3. (a) Write the words before the suffix '-ing' was added.

   managing writing loving having

   ____________ ____________ ____________ ____________

   (b) What letter at the end of each word was dropped before '-ing' was added? ________

4. (a) Write the words before the suffixes '-ed' or '-er' were added.

   arrived completed wiser

   ____________ ____________ ____________

   (b) What letter at the end of each word was dropped before '-ed' or '-er' were added? ________

5. (a) What suffix is added to 'home' to make 'homeless'? ____________

   (b) What does 'homeless' mean? ____________

   ____

   (c) What suffix is added to 'unfortunate' and 'quick' to make 'unfortunately' and 'quickly'? ____________

   (d) Write a sentence using one of these words. ____________

   ____

My learning log	Write **Yes** or **No**. I can recognise words starting with 'wr'. ____________ I can read words containing 'or'. ____________ I know about a range of suffixes. ____________

Nouns

The words we use for people, places and things are called *nouns*.

1. Read the story below.

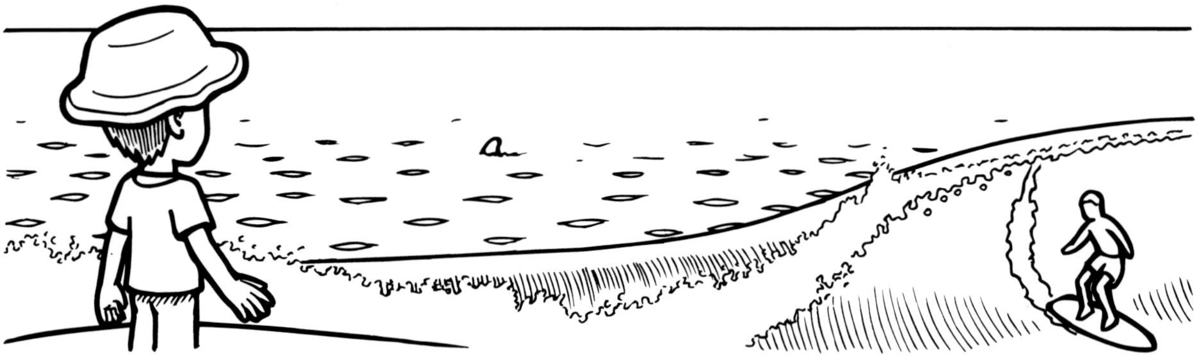

The boy on the beach looked at the surfers on the waves and wished he could surf, too. Then he saw … a fin! Could it be … a shark? He stared, scared, and was about to scream 'SHARK!' when he saw the head of a dolphin pop out of the water. Phew! It was just a dolphin! But, after that, he decided maybe surfing wasn't so great after all!

2. Highlight or colour the words in the story that are ***nouns***.
3. Write them in the table under the correct heading.

people	places	things

4. Tell a partner, write or draw (on the back of this sheet) other nouns that you might see at the beach.

Proper nouns

Some nouns give people, places or things a special name, like Peter, Australia and Band-Aid™. These are called *proper nouns*. They start with a capital letter.

1. Read the story. Underline the proper nouns.

Ben dragged his school bag behind him as he walked inside.

'How was your first day with your new teacher?' asked his mum, Ruby.

'Well, Mum, it was ... a very tiring day', said Ben, as he ate some Tim Tams™. 'Mr James used to hunt crocodiles in Africa, but said he wanted to try something a bit more dangerous! So now he's a teacher!'

'Sounds like you're going to have an interesting year at Brentwood Primary!' said Mum.

2. Write the common noun, then two proper nouns for each picture.

(a)  ____________ ____________, ____________

(b)  ____________ ____________, ____________

(c)  ____________ ____________, ____________

(d)  ____________ ____________, ____________

3. List three proper nouns found in your classroom.

____________ ____________ ____________

The missing cakes

Today, Mum made some little chocolate cakes.

She made them for Tari and Tom to take to school.

She put them on the table to cool.

When Mum went to get them, they were all gone. She was very cross.

'Did you eat the cakes?' she asked Tom.

'No Mum, it was not me', said Tom.

So Mum asked Tari, 'Did you take the cakes?'

'No, Mum, I did not take the cakes', Tari said.

'Where is Sam? Did that greedy dog eat my cakes?' Mum asked.

'No, Sam is outside asleep in his kennel. He did not take the cakes', the children replied.

'What a mystery! What happened to my chocolate cakes? You'll have to take chocolate biscuits to school instead', Mum said.

When they were having tea, Tari told Dad about the cake mystery. Dad's face went very red and he started to laugh.

'It's not funny, it's not funny at all', they told him.

'Yes, it is. I can solve your big mystery.

'I took the cakes.

'I thought you made the cakes for me to take to work for our party. Everyone said they were really delicious.'

Use the narrative on page 3 to complete the page.

1. Title

Write the name of the story.

2. Orientation

(a) When did the story happen? ______________________

(b) Where did it happen? ______________________

(c) Who is the story about? ______________________

3. Complication and events

(a) What was the problem? ______________________

____

(b) Who did Mum ask first? ______________________

(c) Who did Mum ask next? ______________________

(d) How did they know that Sam didn't take the cakes?

____

____

(e) Who told Dad about the mystery? ______________________

4. Resolution

Who took the cakes? ______________________

5. Ending

What happened at the end?

____

____

____

 978-1-912760-62-6 www.prim-ed.com Prim-Ed Publishing

1. Plan a story about something missing.

Title

My story is called

Orientation

When did the story happen? ______________________________

Who is the story about? ______________________________

Where did it happen? ______________________________

Complication

What was the problem?

Events

What happened?

Resolution

Ending

2. Write your story.

3. Check your work.

Make a milkshake

Editing skills

Read the recipe.

Fruity milkshake

Ingredients

- *1 cup of milk*
- *4 big strawberries*
- *1 choped banana*
- *2 scoops of ice-creem*
- *1 teaspoon ov honey*

Method

1. *mix everything in a blenda*
2. *pour the milkshake intoo two glasses*
3. *share it with a frend*

❶ *Punctuation*

(a) Find **3** missing capital letters and **3** full stops.

❷ *Spelling*

(a) There are **6** misspelt words. Underline them then write the correct spelling.

____

____

____

____

____

____

❸ *Grammar*

(a) Write **3** verbs (doing words) from the recipe.

____

____

____

(b) Circle **6** nouns (naming words) in the recipe.

Compound words are made up of two smaller words; for example, 'blueberry', 'something', 'tablespoon'.

(c) Highlight **3** compound words in the text.

Boppy pop

Read the advertisement.

'boppy pop is the newest sweetest lollipop you have ever tasted the flavour gose (threw/through) and (threw/through) and tickles your tastebuds the latest taste sensation on a stick cums in ten tempting flavours and colours it is available to (by/buy) from yor nearest supermarket tast them all to find your favourite flavour be the envy of orl your friends! be the first to try (one/won) today!'

❶ *Punctuation*

(a) Write **8** missing capital letters, **5** full stops and **1** comma in a list.

(b) Circle **2** exclamation marks.

❷ *Spelling*

(a) Circle the correct spelling where a choice of words is given.

(b) There are **5** misspelt words. Underline them then write the correct spelling.

____

____

____

____

____

❸ *Grammar*

Adjectives describe nouns.

(a) Write **3** adjectives from the text to describe a 'Boppy Pop.'

____

____

____

(b) Write a sentence from the text which has 'and' as a 'joining word'.

____

____

____

____

The story of digestion

Editing skills

Read the explanation.

digestion starts with your teeth the food is chewed and mixed with saliva your tongue pushes the food to the back of the throat where muscles squeeze the food down into the stomach digestive juices break down the food it then gets pushed into the small intestine wich soaks up all the goodness. From thair it moves into the large intestine where a lot of worter is taken out. Now, your body doesnt need it any more and pooshes it out wen you go to the toilet

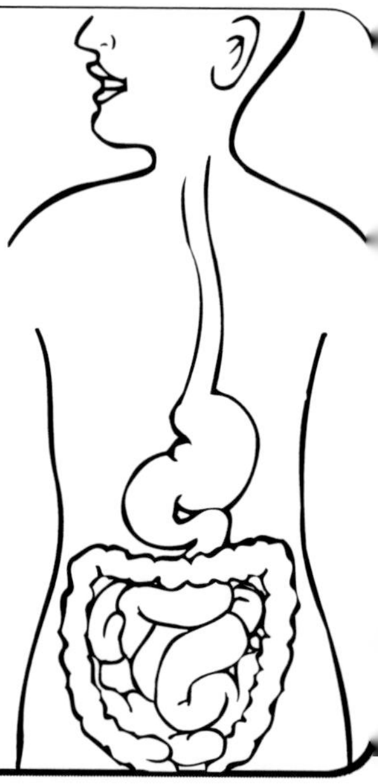

1 *Punctuation*

(a) Write the **5** missing capital letters and **5** full stops.

(b) Find the missing apostrophe.

Contractions are words which have been shortened by taking out letters and adding an apostrophe; for example, 'I have – I've'.

(c) Write the two small words that make up these words.

- didn't ____________________
- I'd ____________________
- we're ____________________
- aren't ____________________
- isn't ____________________

2 *Spelling*

(a) There are **5** misspelt words. Underline them then write the correct spelling above the incorrect words in the text.

3 *Grammar*

(a) Write the verb (doing word) used in the text telling what these things do.

(i) your tongue ____________________

(ii) muscles ____________________

(b) Write an adjective used in the text to describe.

(i) ____________________ juices

(ii) ____________________ intestine

(c) Underline **6** nouns which name body parts.

ODD AND EVEN NUMBERS

N
Number

1. (a) Colour the odd numbers green and the even numbers yellow. Odd numbers always end in 1, 3, 5, 7, 9. Even numbers always end in 2, 4, 6, 8, 0.

1	2	3	4	5	6	7	8	9	10
11	12	13	14	15	16	17	18	19	20
21	22	23	24	25	26	27	28	29	30
31	32	33	34	35	36	37	38	39	40
41	42	43	44	45	46	47	48	49	50
51	52	53	54	55	56	57	58	59	60
61	62	63	64	65	66	67	68	69	70
71	72	73	74	75	76	77	78	79	80
81	82	83	84	85	86	87	88	89	90
91	92	93	94	95	96	97	98	99	100

(b) Did you notice a pattern? yes / no

Describe it. ______________________________

____

2. Fill in the missing numbers.

(a) 30, ______, 34, 36, ______, 40, ______, 44, 46, ______, ______.

(b) 61, 63, ______, 67, ______, ______, 73, 75, ______, 79.

(c) 100, 98, ______, 94, 92, ______, 88, ______, 84, ______, 80.

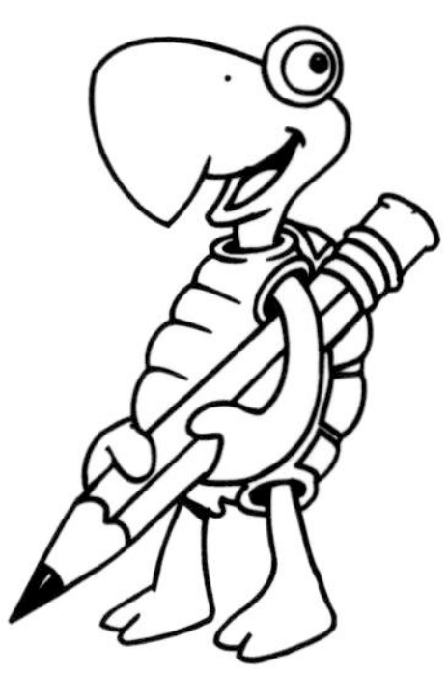

CHALLENGE On the back of the sheet, write the odd numbers backwards from 30 to 1.

Objective ***Recognises odd and even numbers.***

SKIP COUNTING

1. Count in 2s to 100 and colour the numbers in blue. Count in 3s to 100 and circle the numbers. Count in 5s to 100 and write an X over the numbers.

1	2	3	4	5	6	7	8	9	10
11	12	13	14	15	16	17	18	19	20
21	22	23	24	25	26	27	28	29	30
31	32	33	34	35	36	37	38	39	40
41	42	43	44	45	46	47	48	49	50
51	52	53	54	55	56	57	58	59	60
61	62	63	64	65	66	67	68	69	70
71	72	73	74	75	76	77	78	79	80
81	82	83	84	85	86	87	88	89	90
91	92	93	94	95	96	97	98	99	100

2. Fill in the missing numbers. You may like to use the number chart to help you.

(a) 2, 4, ____, ____, 10, ____, 14, 16, ____, ____, 22, ____, 26, ____, 30, ____, 34,

____, 38, 40, ____, 44, ____, 48, ____, 52, 54, ____, 58, 60, ____, 64, ____, 68,

____, 72, 74, ____, ____, 80, ____, 84, 86, ____, ____, 92, ____, 96, ____, 100.

(b) 3, 6, 9, ____, 15, ____, 21, ____, 27, 30, ____, 36, ____, 42, 45, ____, 51, 54, ____,

60, ____, ____, 69, 72, ____, 78, 81, ____, ____,

____, 93, ____, 99.

(c) 5, 10, ____, 20, ____, 30, 35, ____, 45, ____, ____,

60, ____, 70, ____, 80, ____, ____, 95, ____.

CHALLENGE On the back of the sheet, count in fives backwards from 100 to zero.

Objective ***Counts forwards in steps of 1, 2, 3, 5 and 10.***

ADDITION NUMBER STORIES

N Number

1. Read the number story. Set out the number sentence and answer it. Use pictures, counters or place value blocks to help you.

Number story	Picture	Number sentence
(a) John had 5 marbles and he found another 3. How many marbles does he have altogether?		______ + ______ = ______
(b) Elise found 12 flowers in one vase and 15 in another. How many flowers are there altogether?		______ + ______ = ______
(c) There are 24 pupils in 2B and 23 pupils in 2W. How many pupils are there altogether in Year 2?		______ + ______ = ______
(d) 17 pupils catch the bus to school and 4 catch the train. How many are travelling to school on public transport?		______ + ______ = ______
(e) There are 27 bees in one hive and 14 bees in another. How many bees are there altogether?	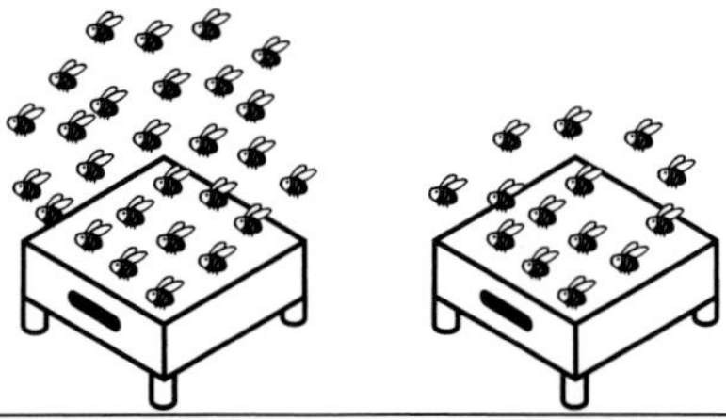	______ + ______ = ______
(f) James has 32 cars and Liam has 28. How many cars do they have altogether?		______ + ______ = ______

CHALLENGE

On the back of the sheet, write your own number story to show this:

12 + 10 = ______

Objective ***Solves addition problems with pictorial representations.***

THE CENTIMETRE (cm)

M Measurement

1. Measure and record the length of the lines using centimetres.

(a)	☐ cm
(b)	☐ cm
(c)	☐ cm

2. Find the actual objects below. Estimate then measure them using your ruler.

Object	Estimate	Measure
(a) 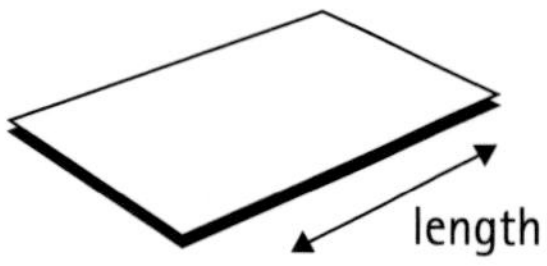	☐ cm	☐ cm
(b) 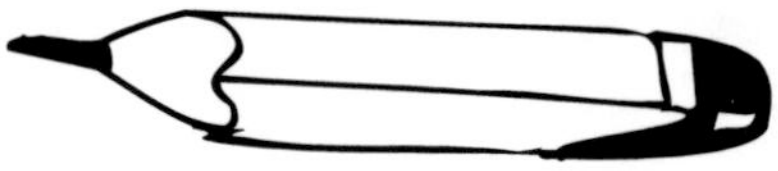	☐ cm	☐ cm
(c) 	☐ cm	☐ cm
(d) 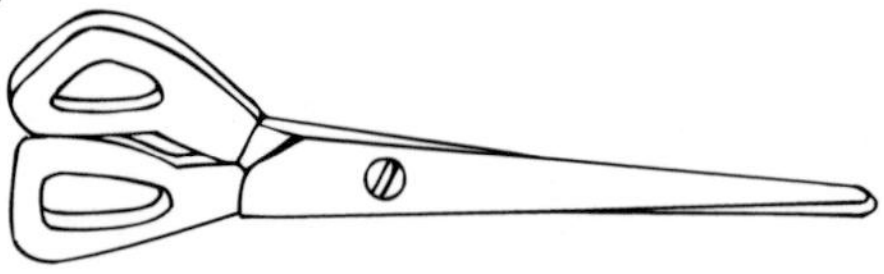	☐ cm	☐ cm

CHALLENGE

If you were to measure the height of a door would you use a 30 cm ruler (cm) or a metre stick (m)? ____________________

Why? ____________________

Objective *Estimates and measures familiar objects using centimetres.*

MORE CENTIMETRES

1. Measure the lines to the nearest centimetre.

(a) = ________ cm

(b) = ________ cm

(c) = ________ cm

(d) = ________ cm

2. Draw straight lines of the following lengths using a ruler.

(a) 3 cm =

(b) 6 cm =

(c) 10 cm =

(d) 12 cm =

3. Measure and record the length of the following objects using centimetres.

(a) pencil = ________ cm

(b) maths book = ________ cm

(c) eraser = ________ cm

(d) sock = ________ cm

(e) chair leg = ________ cm

(f) calculator = ________ cm

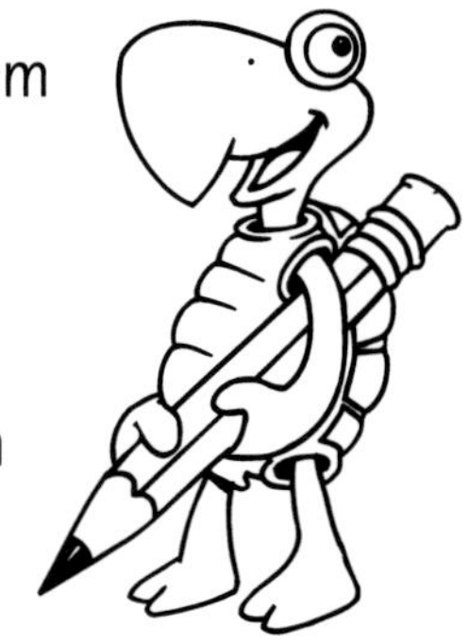

CHALLENGE

Measure and record the length of the classroom, using metres and centimetres. Write the length.

☐ m ☐ cm

Objective ***Reads scale on a ruler to the nearest centimetre.***

2-D SHAPES

1. Trace and name these 2-D shapes.

circle hexagon square octagon rectangle pentagon triangle

(a) 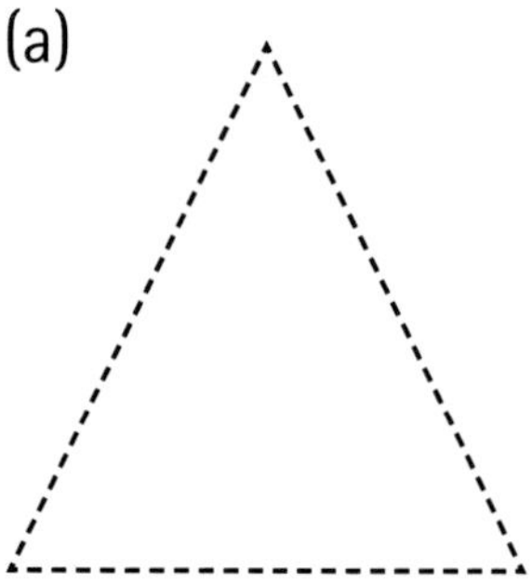	(b) 	(c) 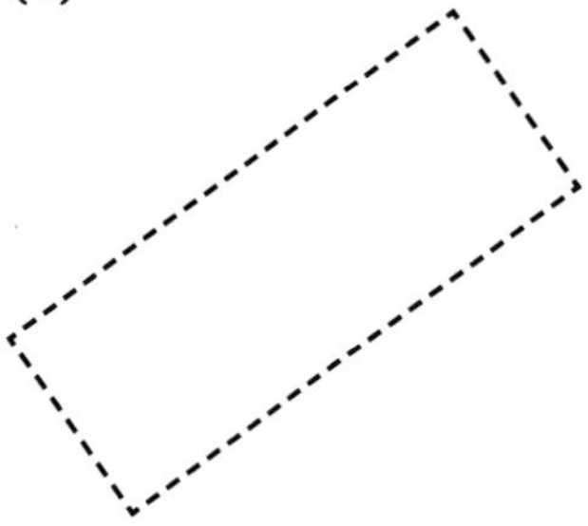	(d) 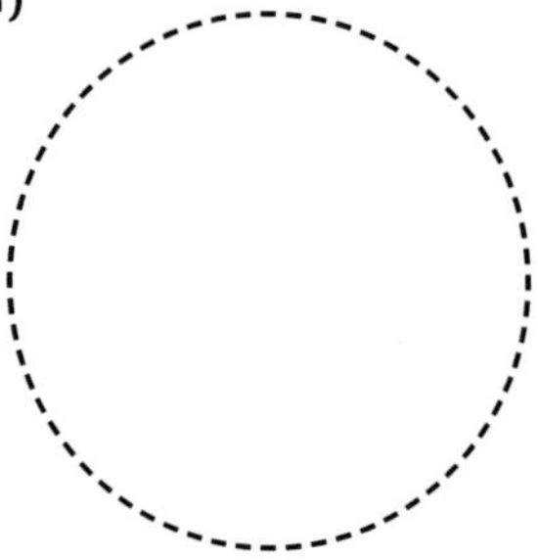
(e) 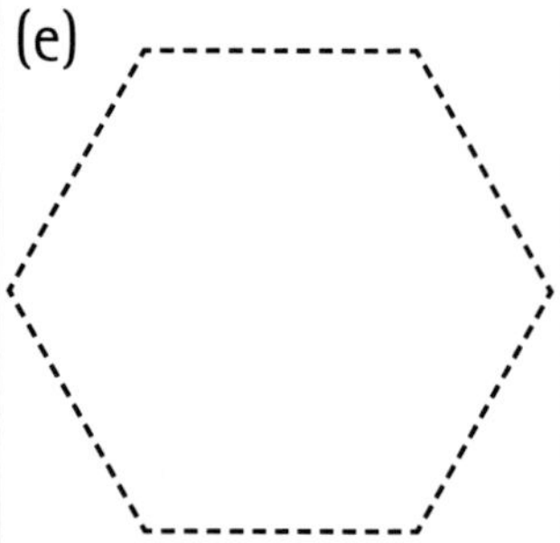	(f) 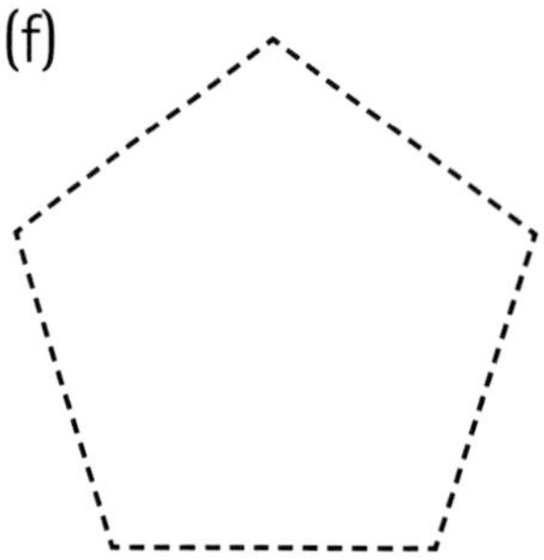	(g) 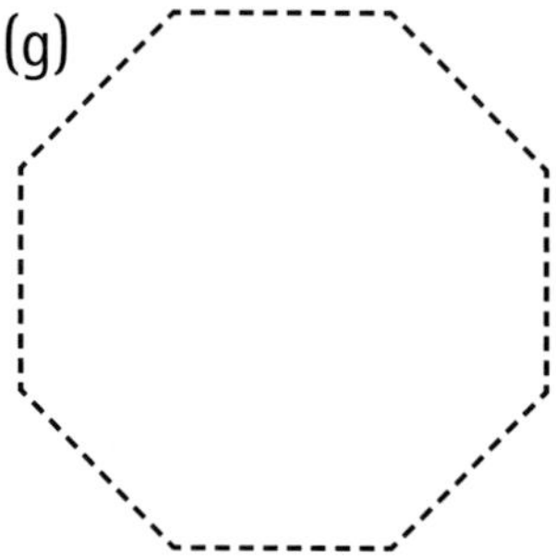	

2. Draw these 2-D shapes.

(a) square	(b) triangle	(c) circle

CHALLENGE

Any shape with four sides is called a **quadrilateral.** On the back of this sheet, draw some quadrilaterals.

Objective	***Identifies and names common 2-D shapes.***

DRAWING BY INSTRUCTION

G Geometry

1. Follow the instructions to reveal the pictures.

(a) *Draw a clown's face with a circle face, triangle hat, crosses for eyes, rectangle mouth and small triangle nose.*	(b) *Draw a house with a triangle roof, square windows, rectangle door and square garage.*

2. Write how many of each shape you need to draw this picture.

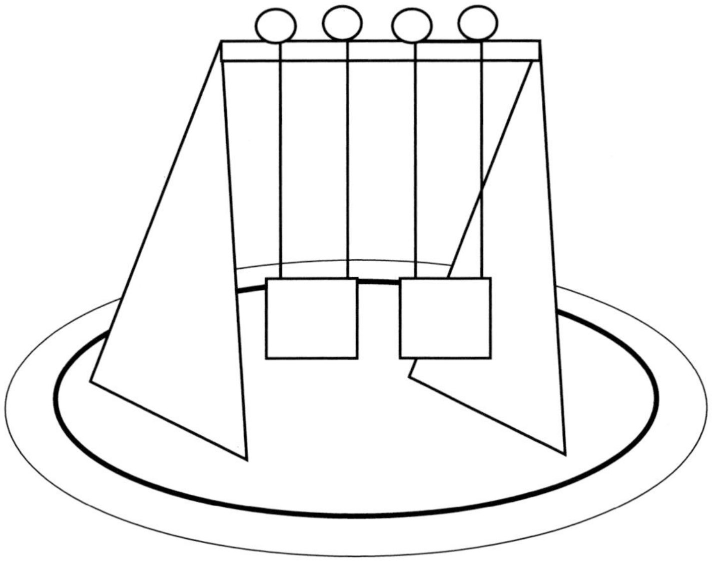

_______ triangles _______ rectangles _______ squares _______ circles

CHALLENGE

With a partner, describe a picture using shapes for him or her to draw onto the back of the sheet. When you have finished, your partner can describe a picture for you to draw.

Objective ***Constructs 2-D shape pictures from instructions.***

Magnets

1 Colour and cut out the pictures below.

2 Sort them under the correct headings on a separate sheet of paper.

Is attracted to a magnet.		Is not attracted to a magnet.	
cotton wool	peg	button	paperclip
screw	scissors	pencil	spoon
safety pin	eraser	key	coin
ruler	zip	book	leaf

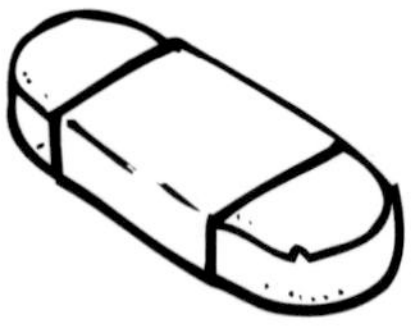

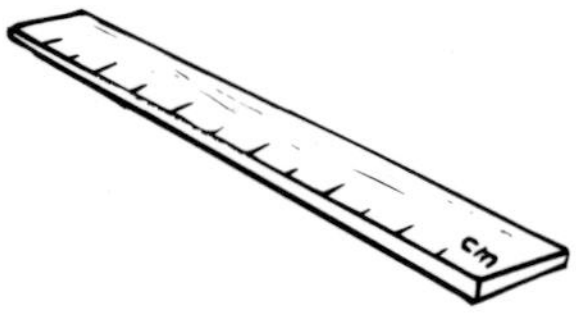

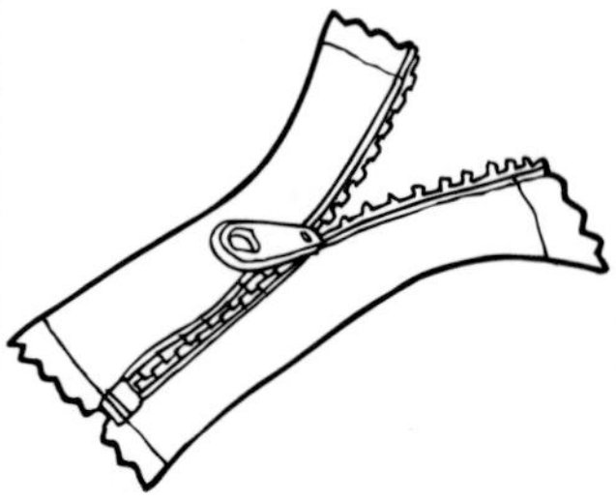

Electricity

1 Finish the sentences.

(a) Electricity gives us h ___ ___ ___.

(b) Electricity gives us l ___ ___ ___ ___.

(c) Electricity gives us p ___ ___ ___ ___.

2 Draw pictures of three things that work using electricity. Label them.

______	______	______

3 Finish the sentences.

(a) Never ______ things into electric sockets.

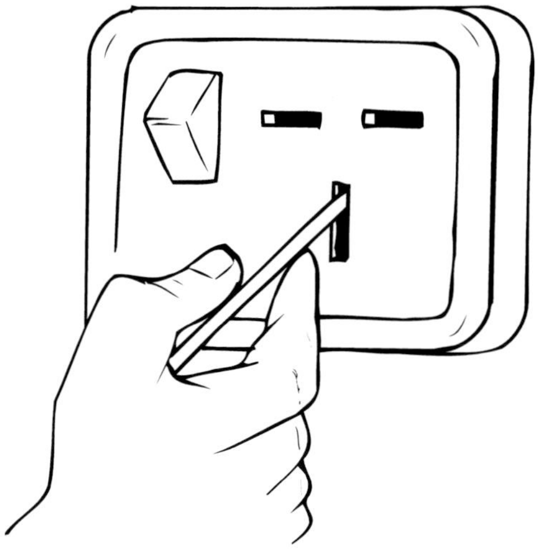

(b) Never touch a socket with ______ hands.

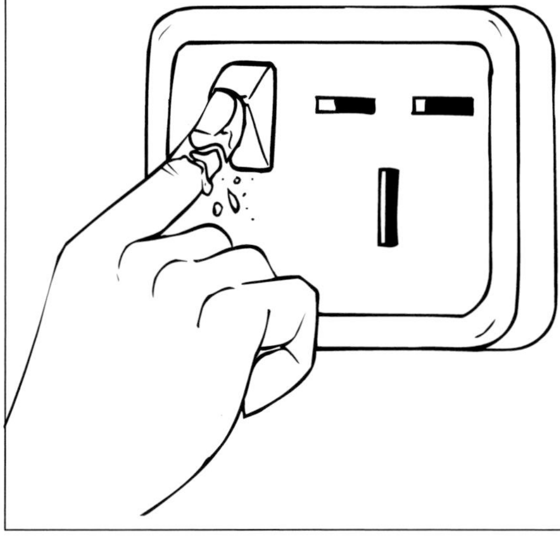

Describing objects

1 Read the words in the boxes.
Choose an object that matches the words.
Draw an object in each box.

Hard	Cold
Fluffy	Can bend

2 Look at each object. Colour the word that describes it best.

pointy	flat
shiny	hard

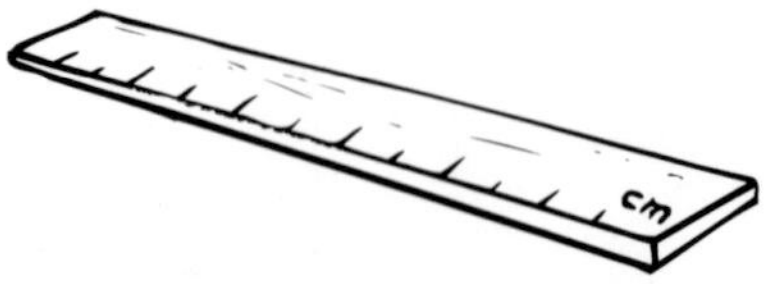

long	round
sharp	short

Grouping objects

1 Read the words in the boxes.
Draw an object in each box and label it.

	Hard	Soft
Round		
Flat		

2 (a) Draw an object in the classroom.

(b) Write two words to describe the object.

____

____

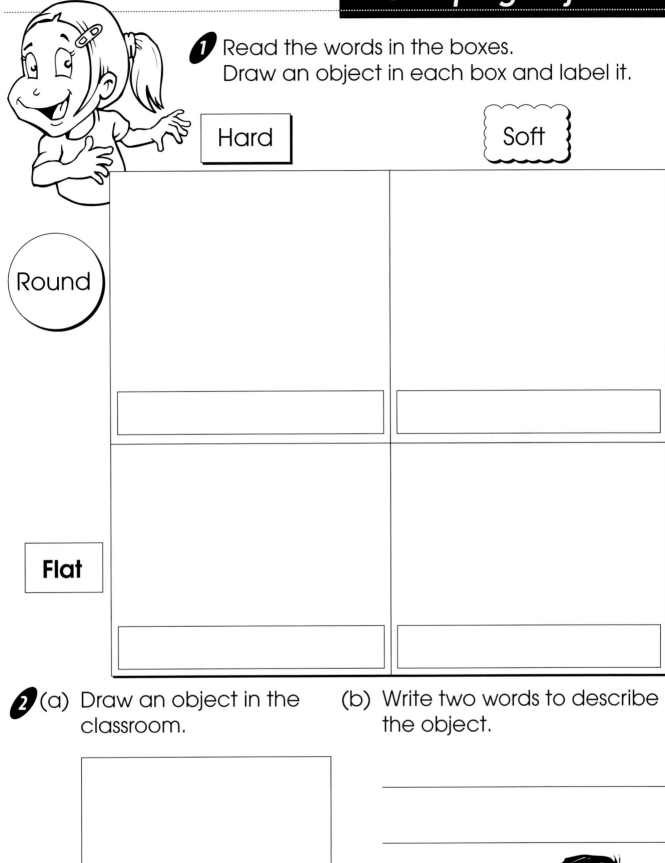

WEEK 2

ENGLISH

Comprehension – The Sword in the Stone 29–31
Comprehension – The Hedley Kow 32–34
Grammar – Verbs 35
Grammar – Command Verbs 36
Writing – Recount, The Family Picnic 37–39
Editing Skills – Let's Go Skateboarding 40
Editing Skills – The Frog Prince 41
Editing Skills – My Washing Line Nest 42

MATHEMATICS

Number – Number Patterns 43
Number – Continue the Pattern 44
Number – Addition Facts 45
Measurement – Comparing Lengths 46
Measurement – The Kilogram (kg) 47
Geometry – Sorting Shapes 48
Geometry – Sorting 2-D Shapes 49

SCIENCE

Forces – How Toys Move 50
Forces – Push or Pull? 51
Forces – Changing Shape 52
Forces – Float or Sink? 53

The Sword in the Stone – 1

Text

Read the poem.

One day a squire young and good
Was lost while walking in the wood.
Arthur was squire to his brother, Kay,
A knight, so brave, most would say.

On this day, Arthur's task was clear
To fetch Kay's sword and bring it near.
But the path through the woods twisted and turned
Until Arthur began to feel concerned.

He followed a muddy track in his search
And, suddenly, came to an ancient church.
At the front of the church, on a monument, stood
A sword in an anvil as proudly as it could.

Thinking that no-one around would care
Arthur pulled out the sword as quickly as he dare.
A nearby path looked quite familiar
So Arthur raced back to Kay with a gift to deliver.

When Kay and his father set eyes on the sword,
They knew at once that Arthur was the chosen lord.
So with one mighty tug of his squire's hands
Arthur became the true king of all the Britons' lands.

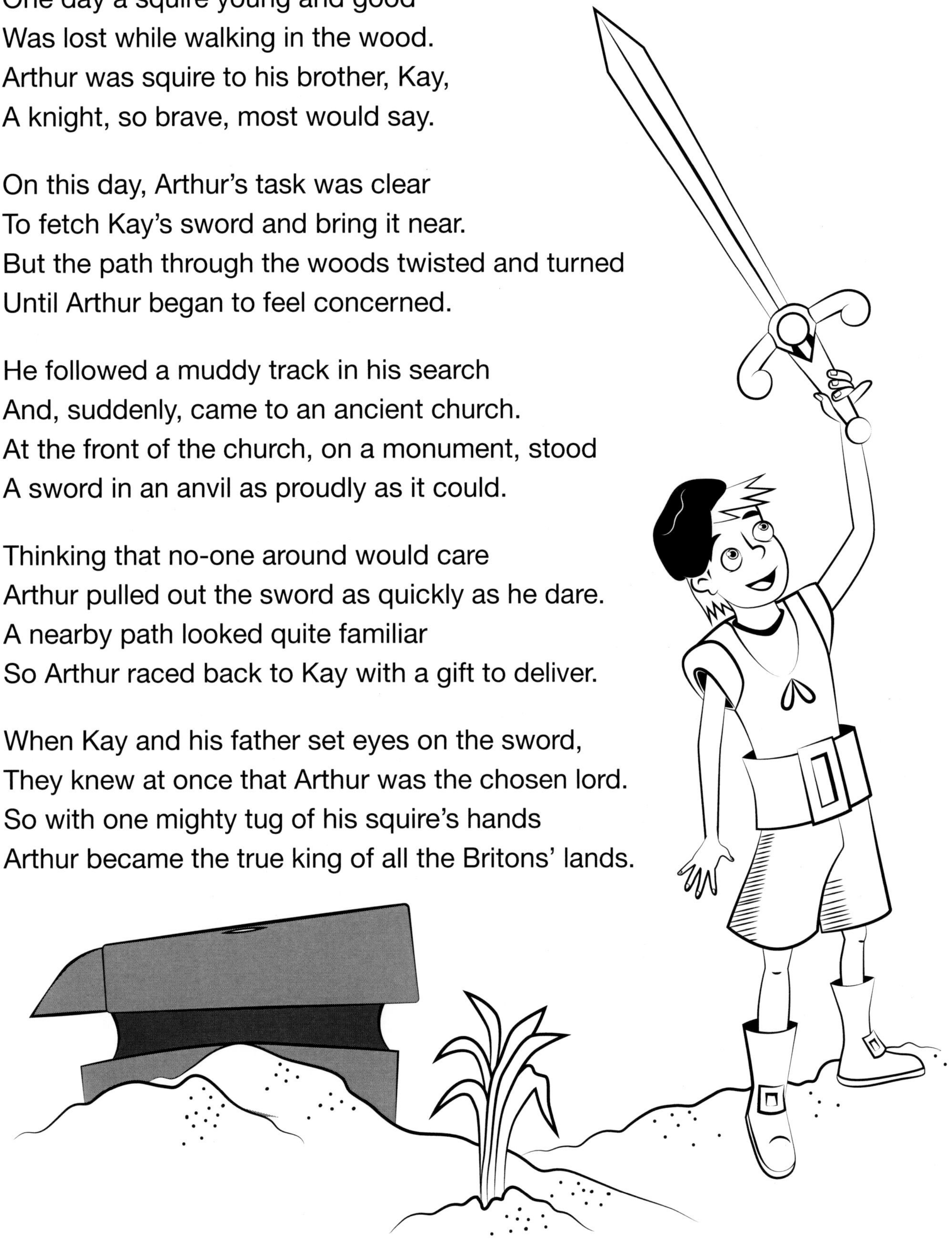

My learning log	When I read this poem, I could read:		
	________ all of it.	________ most of it.	________ parts of it.

The Sword in the Stone – 2

Comprehension

1. Match the words to their meanings.

(a) squire	•	•	a statue, building or structure erected to commemorate an important person or event
(b) monument	•	•	something that has existed for a very long time
(c) ancient	•	•	a young nobleman attending to a knight before becoming a knight himself
(d) anvil	•	•	a heavy iron block on which metal can be hammered and shaped

2. Britons were ______________________________

______________________________.

3. Another word for 'concerned' is ______________________________.

4. Which two occupations from the past are not jobs in the present time?

____

5. What happened to lead Arthur to the sword in the stone?

____

6. Do you think it was just good luck that Arthur found the sword?

Yes No Why? ______________________________

____

7. What do you think happened to the sword afterwards?

____

____

8. Write a word or phrase from the poem you really like.

____

My learning log	While doing these activities:		
	I found Q _____ easy.	I found Q _____ tricky.	I found Q _____ fun.

The Sword in the Stone – 3

Word Reading

1. Write a homophone for each word.

   (a) night ______ (b) new ______ (c) threw ______

   (d) two ______ (e) sew ______ (f) would ______

2. (a) What do the words 'knight', 'know', 'knock' and 'knee' have in common? ______

   (b) Find another word in the poem with these letters. ______

   (c) Write a sentence with two of these words. ______

   ______

3. (a) What do the words 'anvil', 'pencil', 'fossil' and 'nostril' have in common? ______

   (b) Find another word in the poem with these letters. ______

   (c) Write a sentence with two of these words. ______

   ______

4. (a) Which suffix changes 'quick' to 'quickly'? ______

   (b) Which two other words from the poem have the same suffix?

   ______ ______

5. (a) Write the word 'muddy' with the suffix '-er' added so that it means 'more muddy'. (Be careful! You have to change some letters.)

   ______

   (b) Add the suffix '-er' to these words.

   happy ______ lazy ______ heavy ______ funny ______

My learning log	Write **Yes** or **No**. I can recognise homophones. ______ I know words with 'kn' and 'il'. ______ I am aware of the suffixes '-ly' and '-er'. ______

The Hedley Kow – 1

Read the folk tale.

Once upon a time, there was an old woman who was very poor. She had to work very hard in the village to earn a little silver to buy tea and food, but she was always cheerful.

One summer evening as she went home, she spied a stout, black pot lying by the side of the road. Thinking that it must have a hole to have been thrown away, she decided it would make the perfect vessel to hold her flowers. When she looked inside, gold coins gleamed brightly in the bottom of the pot. She felt very lucky to find a pot that had been thrown away. She continued on her way, dragging the pot.

It didn't take long, however, before she grew tired. When she set the pot down, and checked her treasure, the gold had changed into silver.

'Silver is much less trouble than gold', she said to herself, 'I'm still as rich as I need to be. Yes! Silver is fine instead!'

So she went on her way. In a short time, when she stopped to rest, the silver in the pot had become a chunk of iron.

'I am so lucky! No robbers will worry me now!' said the old woman. 'Iron is much better. It will sell for some pennies.'

In the dark, she went on her way. Soon she was weary again. She set the pot down and noticed that the chunk of iron had changed into a stone.

'This is such a fine stone', she stated cheerfully, 'I can use it to hold my door open!'

Finally, she reached home. She set the pot down and opened the gate. Suddenly, the Hedley Kow burst out of the pot and ran away laughing and dancing.

'I am the luckiest creature to see such a sight!' she said. By the warmth of her fire, she thought about how fortunate she was.

The Hedley Kow, of course, was busy looking for someone else to play tricks on!

My learning log	When I read this folk tale, I could read:		
	________ all of it.	________ most of it.	________ some of it.

The Hedley Kow – 2

Comprehension

1. Which common phrase begins this folk tale?

____

2. Which word in the text means:

   (a) a hollow container for holding liquid or other materials? v ________

   (b) strong and thick? s ________

   (c) strong, hard, grey metal? i ________

   (d) small sums of money? p ________

3. In the correct order, write the materials as they appeared in the pot.

____

4. How would you describe the character of the old woman?

____

____

5. What do you think happened to the pot?

____

____

6. Write four interesting words from the text.

________ ________ ________ ________

7. What unusual talent did the Hedley Kow have?

____

____

8. How were the materials in the pot changing each time?

____

____

My learning log	While doing these activities:		
	I found Q _____ easy.	I found Q _____ tricky.	I found Q _____ fun.

The Hedley Kow – 3

Word Reading

1. Underline the letter in the middle of each word that has the same sound as the other words.

treasure	**television**	**usual**

2. Circle the two words with the same sound spelt 'ar' after 'w' like 'towards' and 'war'.

warmth	**who**	**work**	**towards**	**woman**	**away**

3. Underline two words that end with the same sound spelt '-ey' like 'Hedley'.

busily	**cheerfully**	**key**	**chimney**	**lucky**

4. (a) Which word in the text, ending in '-ge', has the same sound as 'age' and 'changed'? It means 'a group of houses smaller than a town'. ______________________

   (b) Write this word in a sentence. ______________________

   ____

5. (a) What suffix has been added to 'cheer' to make 'cheerful'? __________

   (b) The word 'cheerful' means 'full of ______________________'.

   (c) Write the word 'cheerful' in a sentence. ______________________

   ____

6. (a) Add '-est' to these words to make new adjectives. Read the new words.

   fine busy lucky weary

   __________ __________ __________ __________

   (b) Write one of these '-est' words in a sentence.

   ____

   ____

My learning log	Write **Yes** or **No**.
	I can read words with 'ar', 'ey' and 'ge'. __________
	I know about the suffix '-ful'. __________
	I can add '-est' to words to create adjectives. __________

Doing words (Verbs)

1. Read the text.

The beetle swallowed the fly.

The frog frightened the beetle.

The cat scratched the frog.

The dog chased the cat.

The cow bellowed at the dog.

But the kind farmer milked the cow.

***Verbs* or doing words can tell what someone or something is doing.**

2. Copy one verb from the text to answer each question.

(a) What did the beetle do?

The beetle ______________________________ the fly.

(b) What did the frog do?

The frog ______________________________ the beetle.

(c) What did the cat do?

The cat ______________________________ the frog.

(d) What did the dog do?

The dog ______________________________ the cat.

(e) What did the cow do?

The cow ______________________________ at the dog.

(f) What did the kind farmer do?

The kind farmer ______________________________ the cow.

3. Write your own verbs for this sentence.

The farmer's wife ______________________________ the milk.

Command verbs

A *command verb* is a word used to order or command.

1. Read the text.

'March to the left!' said the sergeant.

'Run to the right!' called the lieutenant.

'Turn to centre!' yelled the captain.

'Jog in place!' shouted the major.

'Stop!' ordered the colonel.

'At last!' puffed the private. 'Now I can rest my feet.'

2. Copy five command verbs from the text in the box below.

3. Write the correct command verb in each sentence.

Mix **Butter** **Boil** **Cut** **Colour** **Answer**

(a) ______________________ out the shape.

(b) ______________________ the water.

(c) ______________________ the picture.

(d) ______________________ the telephone.

(e) ______________________ the bread.

(f) ______________________ the cake batter.

4. Complete the sentence.

'_________________, _________________! As fast as you can!
You can't catch me, I'm the gingerbread man.'

 978-1-912760-62-6 www.prim-ed.com Prim-Ed Publishing

The family picnic

On Sunday, Mum, Dad, Jillian, Todd and I went to Fisherman's Point for a picnic for Grandma's birthday.

After we picked up Grandma at eight o'clock, we started the long drive to the picnic spot. We drove past farms with cows and horses and went over a long bridge over a river. Finally, we arrived.

Aunty Beth and Uncle John and our cousins, Susan and Andrew, were waiting for us. We had fun playing games, then we ate lots of birthday cake. Grandma had a nap after lunch on a fold-up chair under the trees.

At 4 o'clock, we packed up the car and headed for home. We all had a great time, especially Grandma, who said that she had never napped in such a nice place!

Use the narrative on page 15 to complete the page.

1. Title

Copy the title.

2. Orientation

Complete the sentence.

On ______________ (when), ______________, ______________ (who), ______________, ______________ (who) and ______________ (who) went to ______________ (where) for ______________ (why)

3. Events

Choose four events and draw them in the correct order.

4. Conclusion

Write words to tell why Grandma had a great time.

Recount plan 1

1. Plan a recount about your own family picnic.

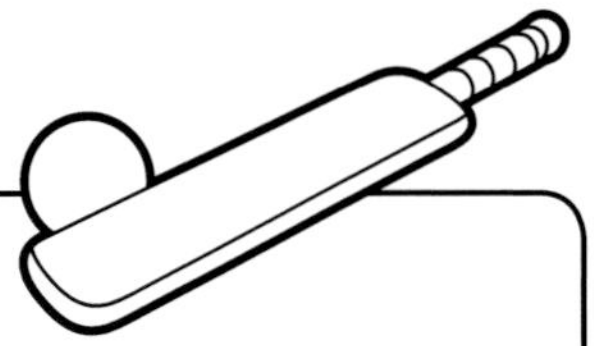

Title

Orientation

Who, when, where, why

Events

What things happened?

Conclusion

What happened at the end?

2. Write your recount.

3. Check your work.

Let's go skateboarding!

Editing skills

Read the recount.

'this is going to be great fun!' shouted adam lowdly as he grabbed his shiny new skateboard and ran quickly out the door he slammed the dore noisily then raced out to the footpath to meet his friend, jordan

'hi adam Let's go!' giggled jordan happily 'i'll ras you to the nearest corna!'

❶ *Punctuation*

(a) Find **4** capital letters at the beginning of a sentence, **4** for proper nouns (people's names), **4** full stops and circle **3** exclamation marks.

(b) Circle the speech marks around the actual words spoken in the text and find **1** comma in a list.

❷ *Spelling*

(a) There are **4** misspelt words. Underline them then write the correct spelling of the misspelt words below.

____

____

____

____

❸ *Grammar*

Recounts use verbs in the past tense. They often end with 'ed'.

(a) Write **4** past tense verbs from the text that end in 'ed'.

____

____

____

____

Contractions are words which have been shortened by taking out letters and adding an apostrophe.

(b) Write **2** contractions from the text.

____

____

The frog prince

Editing skills

Read the narrative.

a frog who was really a prince fetched a ball out of a well for a princess As a reward, the frog ate dinner with the princess he also slept on the princess's pillow wun day, the frog begged the princess to give him a kiss wot a surprise! the frog turned into a handsome prince the prince and princess got married and livd happily ever after

1 *Punctuation*

(a) Find **6** missing capital letters, **6** full stops and circle **1** exclamation mark.

An apostrophe can show that something belongs to a person or thing; for example, the girl's hat. (The hat belongs to the girl.)

(b) Circle an apostrophe in the text which shows ownership.

2 *Spelling*

(a) There are **3** misspelt words. Underline them then write the correct spelling below.

____

____

____

3 *Grammar*

(a) Circle the owner of these things. The apostrophe will help you. It is put *after* the owner or owners.

(i) the frog's legs

(ii) the princess's ball

(iii) the frog's pond

(iv) the princess's castle

(v) the princess's pillow

(vi) the prince's kiss

(vii) the frog's well

(viii) the princess's dinner

(ix) the prince's wedding

My washing line nest

Editing skills

Read the description.

nesst

soft and fluffee

sitting on my lion

waiting for some egs to hatch

as soon az it is time.

berd

small and angree

squawking and flaping at us

waiting for the 'giants' to leeve

goodness! Wot a fuss!

❶ *Punctuation*

(a) Find **10** missing capital letters, one at the beginning of each line of the poem.

(b) Circle **2** exclamation marks and **1** full stop.

❷ *Spelling*

(a) One word in each line has been misspelt. Underline it then write the correct spelling on the line given.

❸ *Grammar*

(a) Write an adjective from the text to describe each noun.

(i) nest ____________________

(ii) bird ____________________

(b) Write **2** verbs in the text that end in 'ing'.

(i) ____________________

(ii) ____________________

NUMBER PATTERNS

N
Number

1. Complete the number patterns and write the rule.

(a) 20, _____, 24, _____, _____, 30, _____, 34, _____, _____, 40.

Rule:

(b) 1, 3, _____, 7, _____, 11, 13, _____, _____, 19, _____.

Rule:

(c) 5, _____, 15, 20, _____, _____, 35, _____, 45, _____.

Rule:

(d) 100, _____, 80, _____, 60, 50, _____, 30, _____, _____.

Rule:

(e) 3, 6, _____, 12, _____, 18, 21, _____, _____, 30.

Rule:

(f) 9, _____, 7, _____, 5, 4, _____, 2, _____, _____.

Rule:

(g) 100, 95, _____, 85, _____, 75, 70, _____, 60, 55.

Rule:

CHALLENGE Look at this pattern and write the rule:

80, 40, 20, 10, 5 Rule: _____

Objective ***Counts in steps of 1, 2, 3, 5 and 10, forwards and backwards.***

CONTINUE THE PATTERN

N Number

1. Continue these number patterns.

   (a) 10 20 30 ________ ________ ________ ________ ________ ________ ________

   (b) 10 9 8 ________ ________ ________ ________ ________ ________ ________

   (c) 3 6 9 ________ ________ ________ ________ ________ ________ ________

   (d) 5 10 15 ________ ________ ________ ________ ________ ________ ________

   (e) 60 58 56 ________ ________ ________ ________ ________ ________ ________

2. Count by odd numbers to complete this dot-to-dot picture.

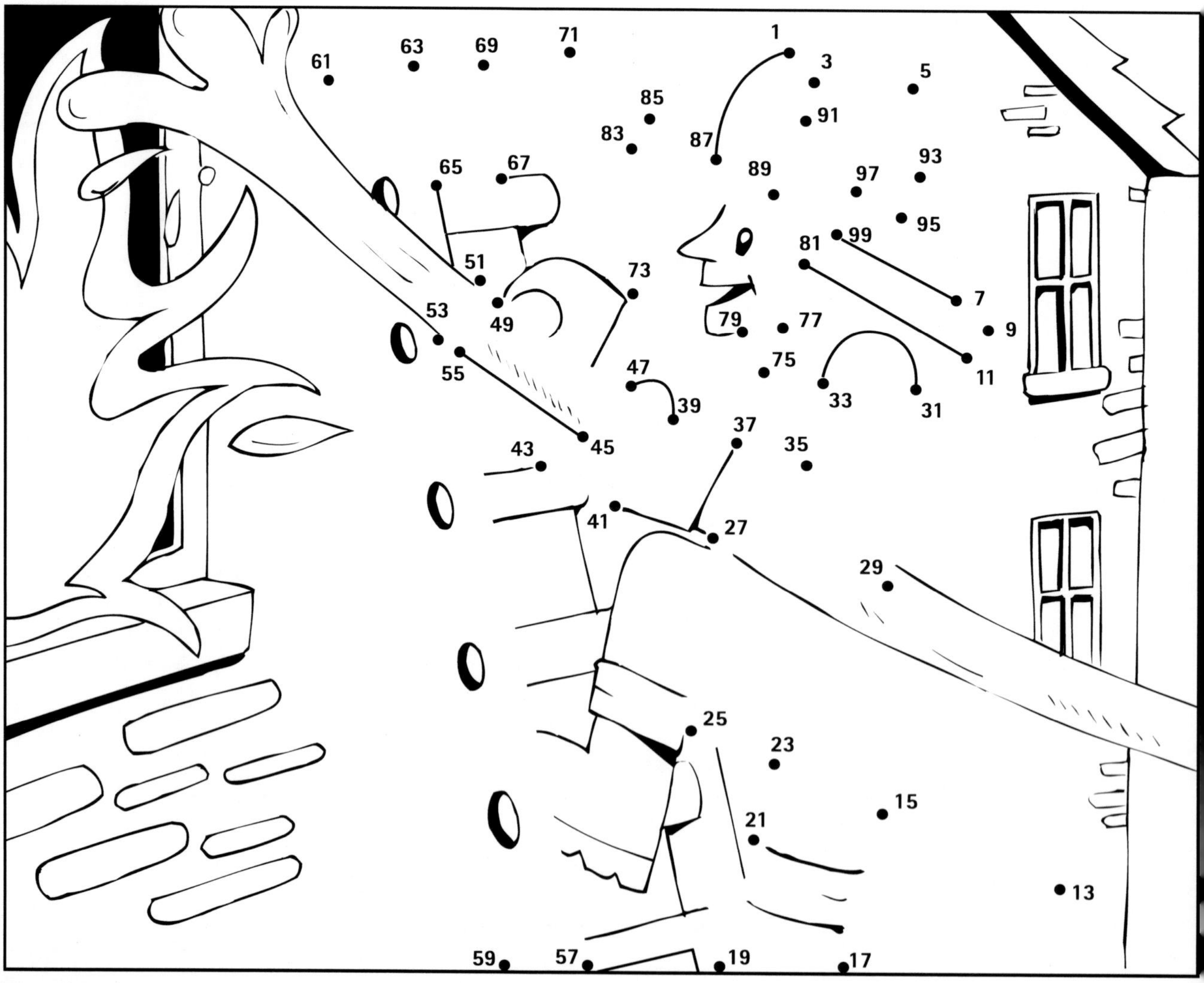

CHALLENGE (a) Continue this number pattern:

40, 38, 36, ____, 2

(b) On the back of this sheet, write how you solved this problem.

Objective ***Counts in steps of 1, 2, 3, 5 and 10, forwards and backwards.***

ADDITION FACTS

N Number

1. Add these pictures and circle the correct answer.

	+		=	6 7 8
	+		=	11 12 13
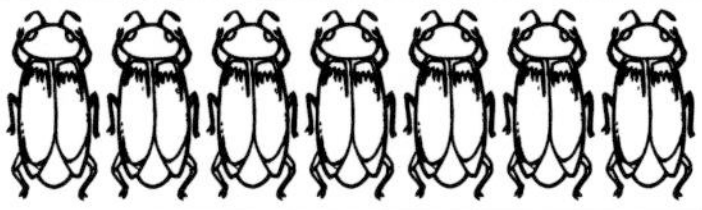	+	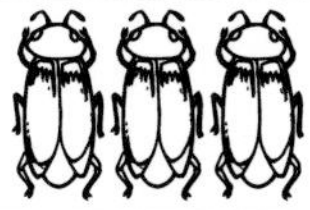	=	8 9 10
	+		=	11 12 13
	+		=	11 12 13
	+		=	15 16 17

2. Answer and circle all the sums that add up to 10.

(a) 6 + 4 = _____ (b) 3 + 8 = _____ (c) 8 + 2 = _____ (d) 7 + 3 = _____ (e) 9 + 2 = _____

(f) 4 + 5 = _____ (g) 1 + 9 = _____ (h) 5 + 6 = _____ (i) 5 + 5 = _____ (j) 3 + 8 = _____

3. Answer and circle all the sums that add up to 20.

(a) 10 + 10 = _____ (b) 5 + 14 = _____

(c) 15 + 5 = _____ (d) 12 + 8 = _____

(e) 9 + 10 = _____ (f) 14 + 6 = _____

(g) 9 + 11 = _____ (h) 17 + 3 = _____

(i) 11 + 11 = _____ (j) 13 + 7 = _____

CHALLENGE

Use counters or a number line to solve these addition sums:

(a) 12 + 7 = _______ (b) 16 + 9 = _______ (c) 19 + 8 = _______

Objective ***Mentally calculates addition facts to 20.***

COMPARING LENGTHS

Length means how long an object is.

1. Colour the longer item in each pair.

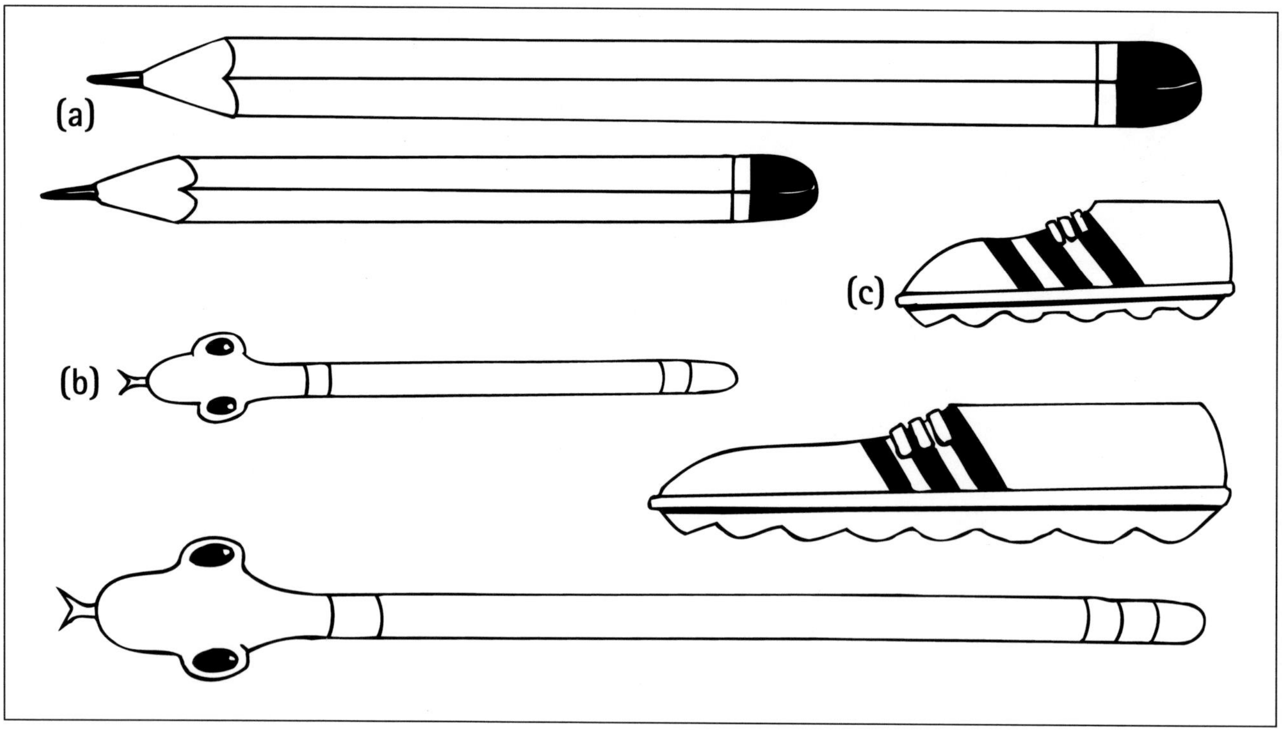

2. Write the symbols < less than, > more than, and = equal to.

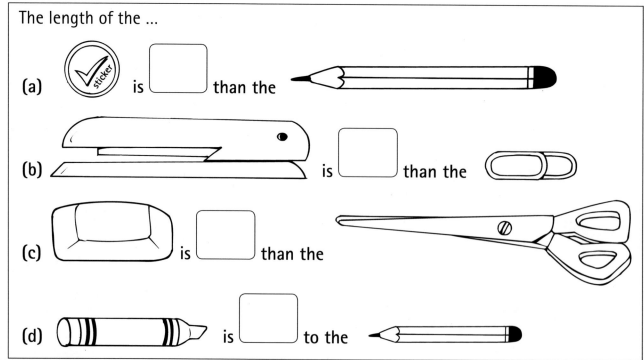

The length of the ...

(a) 

is ☐ than the 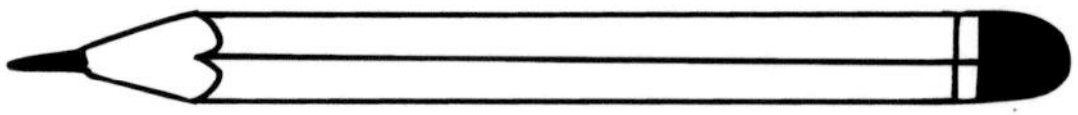

(b) 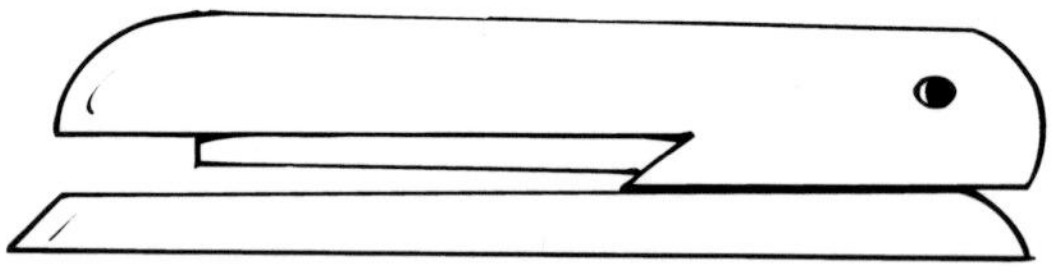 is ☐ than the 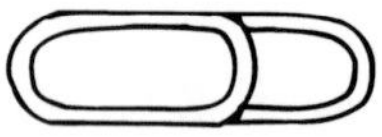

(c) 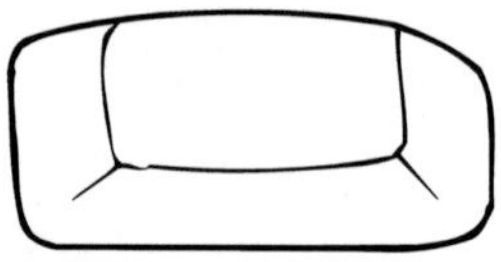 is ☐ than the 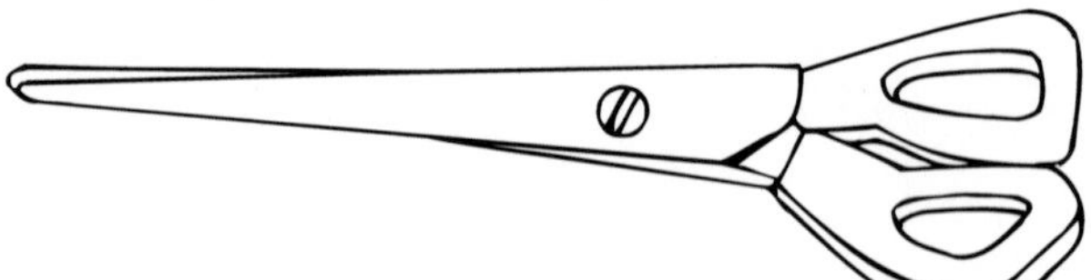

(d) 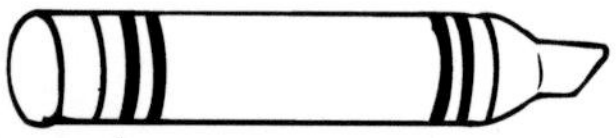 is ☐ to the 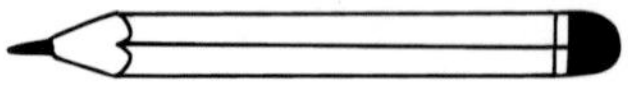

CHALLENGE

Find and write things with lengths:

(a) < your pencil (b) > your pencil (c) = your pencil

Objective *Identifies the length of everyday objects using symbols <, > and =.*

THE KILOGRAM (kg)

1. Hold a kilogram weight in one hand and one of these objects in the other. Tick the box to describe the objects compared to the kilogram.

Object	Heavier	Lighter	The same
(a) 			
(b) 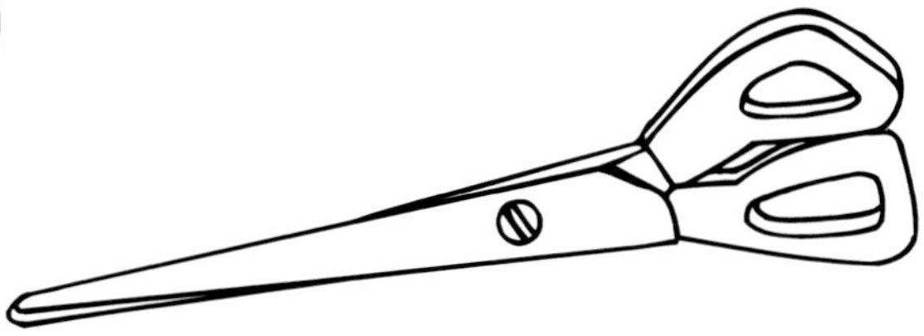			
(c) 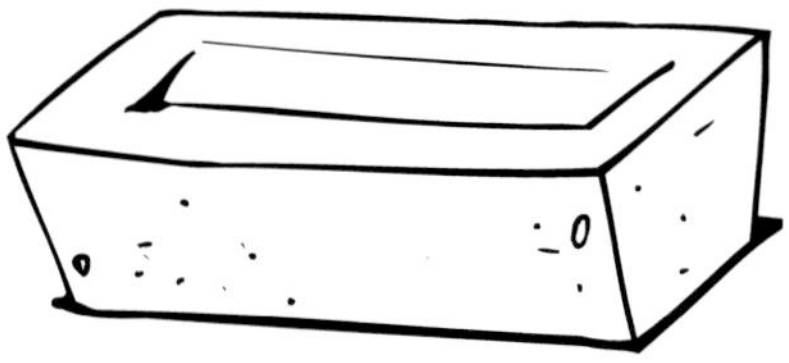			
(d) 			

2. Use a balance scale and weights (kilograms and $^1/_2$ kilograms) to estimate and weigh these objects.

(a) 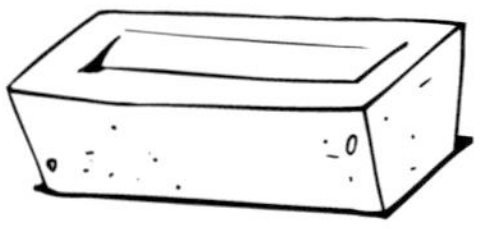	Estimate ______________ kg	Measure ______________ kg
(b) 	Estimate ______________ kg	Measure ______________ kg
(c) 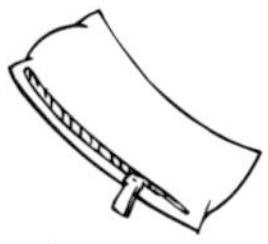	Estimate ______________ kg	Measure ______________ kg

CHALLENGE Colour the objects you would measure using kitchen or balance scales blue and the objects you would measure using bathroom scales red.

grapes	reading book	dog	full rucksack	beads	child

Objective ***Measures familiar objects using balance scales and kilograms.***

SORTING SHAPES

1. Colour the shapes with the same number of sides the same colour.

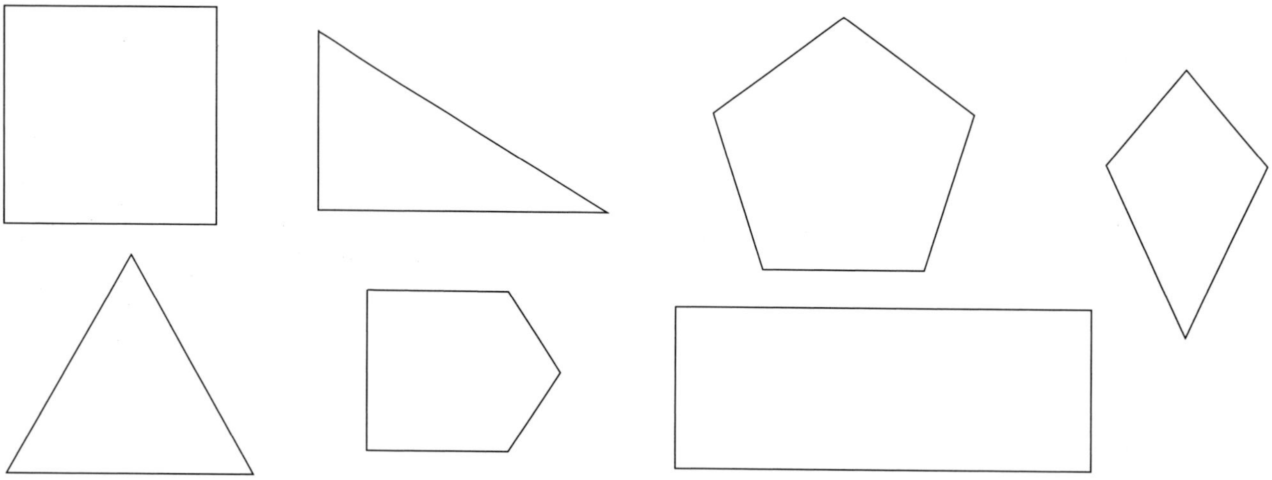

2. How many shapes?

(a) Have 3 sides? ☐

(b) Have 4 sides? ☐

(c) Have 5 sides? ☐

3. Draw the shapes onto the correct place on the table.

shapes with 3 sides	shapes with 4 sides	shapes with 5 sides

CHALLENGE

On the back of the sheet, draw a different shape that has four sides.

Shapes with four sides are called **quadrilaterals.**

Objective ***Sorts shapes according to number of sides.***

 978-1-912760-62-6 www.prim-ed.com Prim-Ed Publishing

SORTING 2-D SHAPES

1. Look at the shapes and draw them under the correct heading.

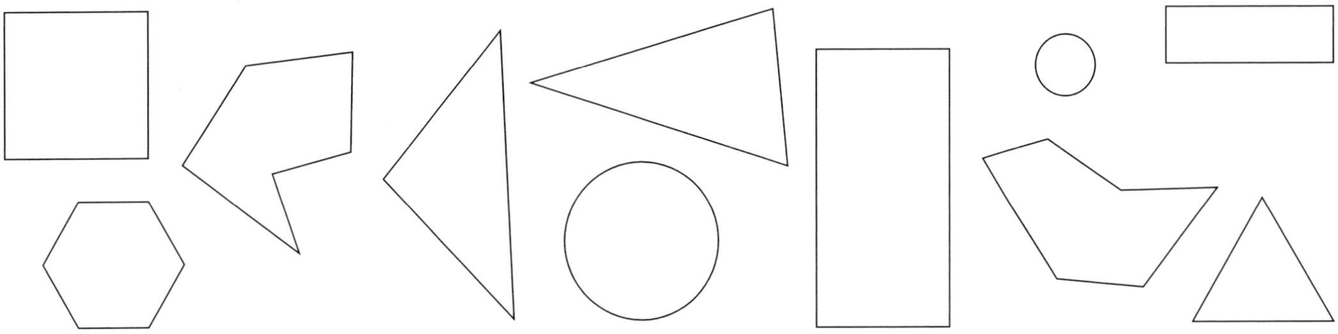

(a) Four sides and four corners.	(b) Three sides and three corners.
(c) No corners and no sides.	(d) Six corners and six sides.

CHALLENGE

On the back of the sheet, draw a shape to match this description: eight sides and eight corners.

Objective ***Classifies shapes using simple criteria.***

How toys move

1 Match each toy to the way it moves.
Some may move more than one way.

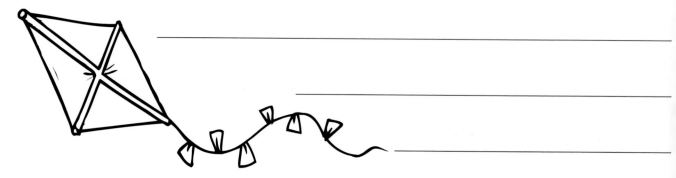

2 How does this toy move? ______________________

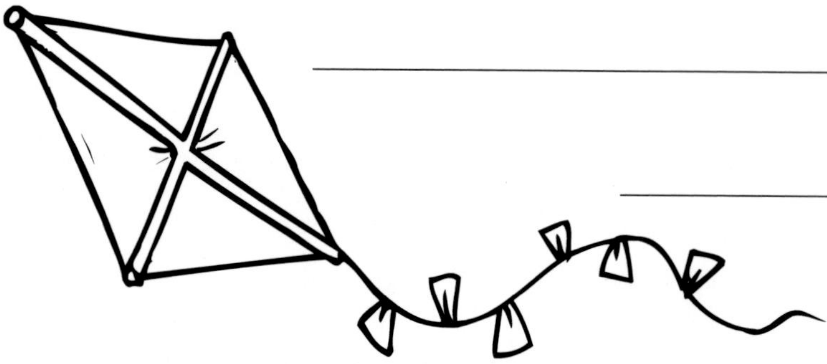

Push or pull?

1 Tick whether you need to push or pull these objects to make them move. Some may be both.

Object	Push	Pull	Both
tissue box 			
shopping trolley 			
electric switch 			
computer keyboard 			
kite 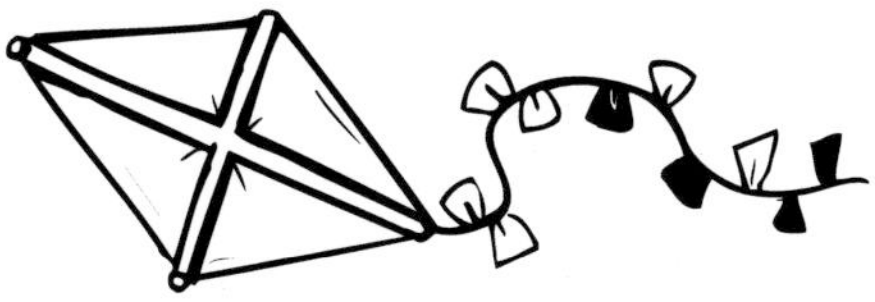			

2 Draw and label one different object for each box.

Push	Pull	Both

Changing shape

1 Complete the table. These words will help you.

bend **stretch** **twist** **squash**

2 Choose two more objects and test them.

Object	Can change shape	Cannot change shape	Describe how you changed it	Can it change back?
(a) elastic band 				
(b) stone 				
(c) stick 				
(d) sponge 				
(e) sheet of paper 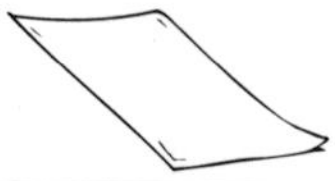				
(f)				
(g)				

Float or sink?

1 Draw six objects you used.
Does each float or sink?
Have a guess before you try.

Object	Guess	Float or Sink

2 Did any sink slowly? Draw or write them.

WEEK 3

ENGLISH

Comprehension – Woodland Habitats 55–57
Comprehension – Wally Woodlouse's Adventure 58–60
Grammar – Adjectives 61–62
Writing – Procedure, Summer Fun 63–65
Editing Skills – Make a Sandwich 66
Editing Skills – The Missing Clown 67
Editing Skills – Ned the Elephant 68

MATHEMATICS

Number – Patterns and Rules 69
Number – Match the Number 70
Number – Adding 71
Number – Methods of Subtraction 72
Measurement – Comparing Mass 73
Measurement – Measurement 74
Geometry – Shapes in Pictures 75
Geometry – Describing 2-D Shapes 76

SCIENCE

Caring for My Locality – My Tree 77
Caring for My Locality – My Environment 78
Caring for My Locality – Caring for My Environment 79

Woodland Habitats – 1

Text

Read the report.

A **habitat** is a natural environment or home of a variety of plants and animals. There are a variety of different habitats like woodlands, seashore, ocean or rainforest. Each one is special.

A **woodland** is a habitat made up mostly of trees. The two main types of woodland habitats are those made up of conifers (fir trees) and those made up of broadleaf trees.

Woodland habitats have a number of layers that provide food and shelter for many different animals.

- The top layer is a canopy of tall trees that overlap and link together. Many birds, insects like aphids and leaf miners, and fungi are found in the canopy.
- The understorey, or shrub layer, is made up of smaller trees. Nesting birds, small mammals, insects and other invertebrates (animals without a backbone) are found in the shrub layer.
- The field layer has wildflowers, grasses, brambles and gorse. Small animals, bees, butterflies and other insects can be found in the field layer.

- The ground layer is made up of mosses, liverwort, ferns, grasses, herbs, mushrooms and toadstools, fallen and decaying wood, and leaf litter. Insects, caterpillars and other invertebrates are found in the ground layer.

The layers, plants and animals in a woodland are different. The amount of light coming through the canopy affects the plants that can grow in the layers underneath. Sometimes the canopy is very widespread so more plants can grow down below. The more plants there are, the more animals can be found.

Woodlands have been neglected or cleared for farming, cities and motorways. Many woodland animals have lost their habitats. It is very important to save these very special habitats.

My learning log	When I read this report, I could read:		
	________ all of it.	________ most of it.	________ parts of it.

Woodland Habitats – 2

Comprehension

1. In words or short phrases, write three pieces of information from the text.

- ______________________________
- ______________________________
- ______________________________

2. The word 'habitat' means ______________________________

______________________________.

3. Write a list of six plants and/or animals you knew before reading the text.

__________ __________ __________

__________ __________ __________

4. Write a list of four plants and/or animals that you did not know before reading the text.

__________ __________

__________ __________

5. Choose one plant or animal from question 4 and write a question that will give you more information about it.

____

____

6. (a) Describe what it would be like in the ground layer.

____

(b) Why would plants or animals like living in this layer?

____

____

7. What might happen if woodlands were destroyed?

____

My learning log	While doing these activities:		
	I found Q ______ easy.	I found Q ______ tricky.	I found Q ______ fun.

Woodland Habitats – 3

1. Write each word with a slash (/) to separate the syllables.

   (a) environment ________________

   (b) habitat ________________

   (c) canopy ________________

   (d) understorey ________________

   (e) invertebrates ________________

2. Join the pairs of words to make compound words.

   (a) wood + lands = ____________ (b) toad + stools = ____________

   (c) rain + forest = ____________ (d) butter + fly = ____________

   (e) wild + flowers = ____________ (f) sea + shore = ____________

3. (a) Change the singular noun 'canopy' to plural (more than one) by adding the suffix '-es'. (You need to change a letter.) ____________

   (b) Add the suffix '-es' to this other word from the text.

   variety ____________

4. (a) What two letters are used to spell the sound 'l' in 'animal' and 'mammal'? ____________

   (b) Find and write two other words in the text that end in these two letters.

   ____________ ____________

5. (a) Find and write four words in the text with the 'or' sound spelt 'all'.

   ________ ________ ________ ________

   (b) Write a sentence using two of these words.

   ____

My learning log	Write **Yes** or **No**. I can divide some words into syllables. ________ I know what a compound word is. ________ I can read words containing 'al' and 'all'. ________

Wally Woodlouse's Adventure – 1

Read the narrative text.

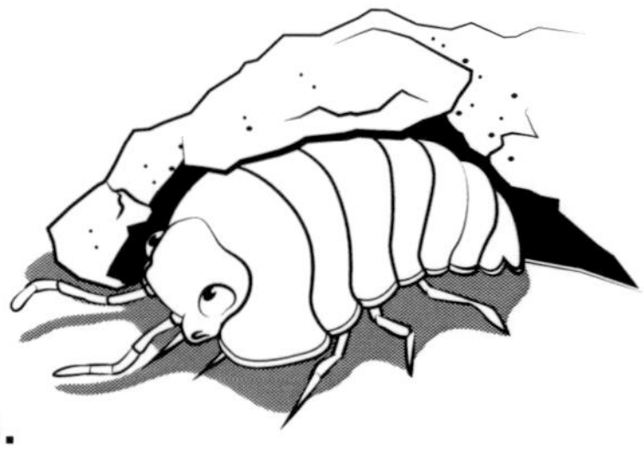

Wally Woodlouse poked his smooth, grey head out from under the leaves and looked around. The dark, damp, dead leaves and decaying matter provided a cool place to live and a good food source.

It was night-time. The air was cool and damp. It was the best time for feeding and having adventures.

Wally came out from his micro-habitat. Seven pairs of legs carried his smooth, rounded body over the ground. Wally's two pairs of antennae wiggled in the dark. They helped him feel and smell his way around.

Over squishy berries, under a log and around a stone, Wally clambered. He stopped frequently to dampen his body in dew and wet leaf litter. It was important to keep damp because otherwise breathing would be impossible. A woodlouse who dried out died very quickly.

Wally's head, thorax and abdomen formed a smooth outline as he moved carefully from one hiding place to the next. Woodlice aren't the only nocturnal creatures active at night!

Suddenly, a nasty toad lumbered out from a nearby shrub. Wally stopped and slid quietly beneath a rock. Pesky toads! They were always bothering innocent woodlice when they venture out at night! Life in a woodland could be very dangerous for a little woodlouse having a night-time adventure.

After a short time, the toad jumped away and Wally moved on. Ground beetles, centipedes, spiders and a mousey shrew passed close to Wally. Every time, Wally crept into a hiding place until they had passed by. Sometimes, Wally stopped to nibble on leaves and mangled fruit. He needed to continue his journey.

Soon, the darkness lightened and Wally knew morning was coming. He hurried back to his home in the undergrowth to sleep and think about his adventure. He couldn't wait for the next one!

My learning log	When I read this narrative, I could read:		
	________ all of it.	________ most of it.	________ parts of it.

Wally Woodlouse's Adventure – 2

Comprehension

1. Why did Wally come out of his hiding place at night-time?

____

2. What would happen to Wally if he had to feed during the day?

____

____

3. What would happen if Wally did not keep his body damp?

____

4. What does a woodlouse look like? ______________________________

____

____

5. What word describes an animal who sleeps during the day and feeds at night?

____

6. Copy three phrases that describe when or how events happened.

____

____

7. Which word means:

   (a) a very small habitat? ______________________________

   (b) long, thin sensory organs on the heads of creatures like woodlice?

   ____

8. Copy a sentence or phrase that you like from the text.

____

____

My learning log	While doing these activities:		
	I found Q ______ easy.	I found Q ______ tricky.	I found Q ______ fun.

Wally Woodlouse's Adventure – 3

1. Circle the 'tricky' parts of these words.

passed	his	he	every	was	grey	nasty

2. (a) The punctuation mark in the title is called an ______________________.

   (b) What does it do? ______________________

   (c) What other word from the text has the same punctuation mark, for the same reason? ______________________

3. (a) Write the contraction 'aren't' as two words. ______________________

   (b) Write another contraction from the text. ______________________

4. (a) What do the words 'wriggle', 'beetle' and 'mangle' have in common?

   ____

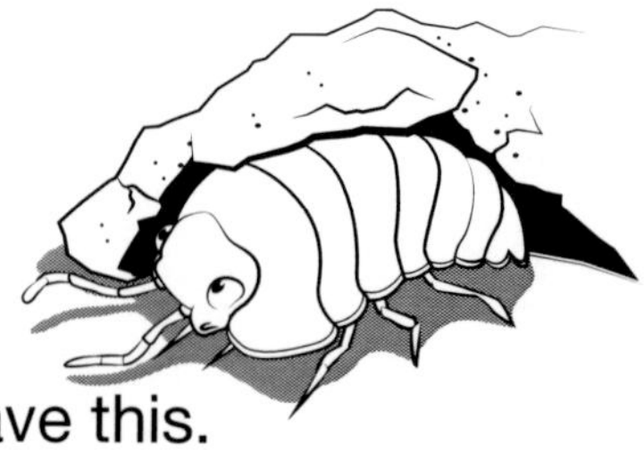

   (b) Find and write three more words in the text that have this.

   ____________ ____________ ____________

   (c) Write a sentence using two of these words.

   ____

5. (a) Underline the two words in the box that have the same sound at the end as 'valley' and 'monkey'.

journey	by	way	they	always
quietly	grey	every	mousey	nearby

   (b) What do these words have in common?

   ____

6. Make other words like 'hiding' by adding the suffix '-ing'.

   (a) hurry ____________ (b) venture ____________

   (c) carry ____________ (d) come ____________

My learning log	Write **Yes** or **No**. I can recognise apostrophes for ownership and contraction. ____________ I can read words containing 'le' and 'ey'. ____________ I know about the suffix '-ing'. ____________

 978-1-912760-62-6 www.prim-ed.com Prim-Ed Publishing

Describing words – 1

An *adjective* is a describing word.

1. Read the story. Circle each describing word.

The shopping trip

I helped Mum do the shopping on Saturday. First, we went to buy Dad a blue shirt with a striped tie to match. Then, we went to get Mum some shoes. She picked out a pair of gold sandals.

After that, it was time to buy the food. From the bakery, we bought a loaf of white bread. In the greengrocer we chose ripe bananas, green grapes, a juicy watermelon and large, red tomatoes. We bought roast beef and fresh mince at the butcher's.

Finally, in the supermarket, we bought a long list of things. Mum let me choose a bottle of cold lemonade to drink at home!

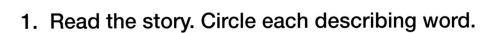

2. Draw what was bought for each person or in each shop. Circle the describing words with coloured pencil.

Dad *striped tie*	**Mum** *gold sandals*
Bakery *white bread*	**Child's treat** *cold lemonade*
Butcher *roast beef* *fresh mince*	**Greengrocer** *ripe bananas* *juicy watermelon* *green grapes* *large, red tomatoes*

Describing words – 2

An *adjective* is a describing word.

1. (a) Find the words in the word search.

brown
funny
tiny
heavy
kind
pretty

p	r	e	t	t	y	h	f
k	h	e	a	v	y	n	u
i	x	p	p	y	h	g	n
n	t	t	i	n	y	y	n
d	u	b	r	o	w	n	y

(b) Choose one of the words to complete each sentence.

(i) I helped Mum put the ______________ flowers in a vase.

(ii) Please be careful lifting that ______________ box.

(iii) The little ______________ bear cub was very cute.

(iv) We watched the ______________ ant hurry into its nest.

(v) When Jason told a ______________ joke, we all laughed.

(vi) I held the door open for the ______________ lady.

2. Make up three sentences so that each of these words describes something.

tall	yellow	hard

(a) ____

____

(b) ____

____

(c) ____

____

 978-1-912760-62-6 www.prim-ed.com Prim-Ed Publishing

Summer fun

Finish this summer picture.

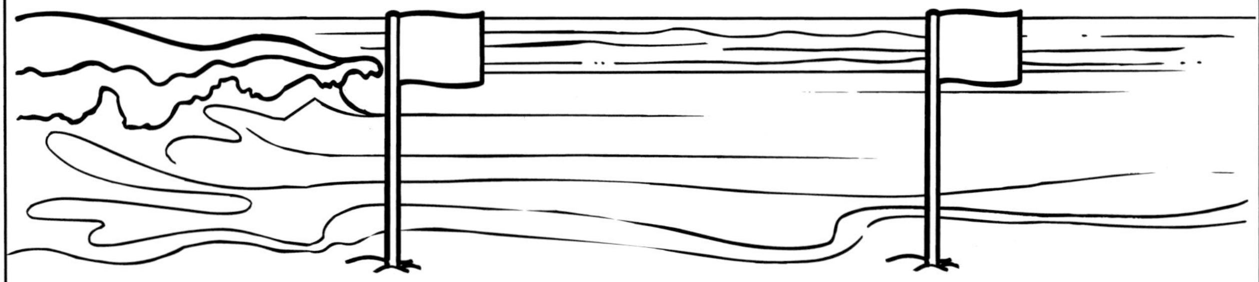

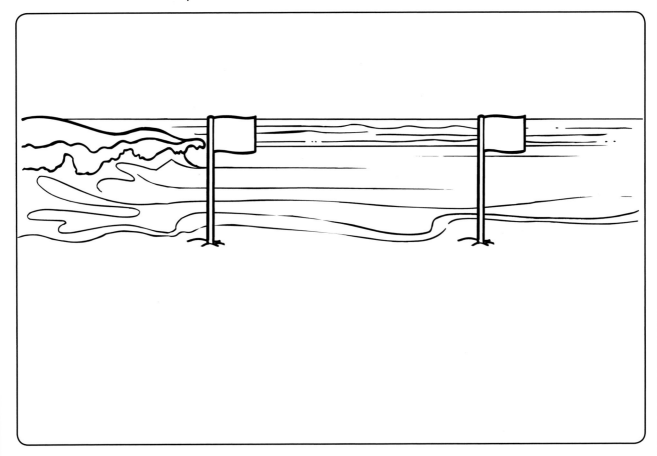

You will need:

- a lead pencil
- coloured pencils or felt-tipped pens

Steps:

1. Draw a boy and a girl swimming between the flags.
2. Draw someone surfing in the waves on a red surfboard.
3. Draw a yellow and green beach umbrella in the sand.
4. Draw a sandcastle next to it.
5. Draw a blue bucket and spade in the sand.
6. Draw an airplane in the sky.
7. Colour the flags red and yellow.
8. Colour the rest of the picture.

Test: Does your picture look good? ________________________

Use the procedure on page 27 to complete the page.

1. Title

2. Goal

The procedure tells you how to …

____

____

3. Needs

Draw and label the things you will need.

4. Steps

(a) How many steps are there? ______

(b) Write the two words used at the beginning of the steps.

(i) ______________________

(ii) ______________________

(c) These words are called

____

(d) Write three more of these types of words.

____

____

____

5. Test

How would you know if the procedure was right?

1. Plan a procedure.

Title

Goal

To finish a picture about meeting an alien.

Needs

Steps

Put your steps in order.

1. ______________________

2. ______________________

3. ______________________

4. ______________________

5. ______________________

6. ______________________

Test

How would you know if the procedure was right?

2. Check your work.

Make a sandwich

Editing skills

Read the procedure.

Ingredients

– 2 slices of bred – butter or margarine ______________

– grated chees – slices of tomato ______________

– slice ov ham – lettuce ______________

- *collect orl the ingredients* ______________
- *spred the margarine on the bread* ______________
- *put the fillings on won slice of bread* ______________
- *poot the second slice of bread on top* ______________
- *cut the sanwich into two large triangles* ______________

❶ *Punctuation*

(a) Find **5** capital letters at the beginning of sentences and **5** full stops.

❷ *Spelling*

(a) One word in each line has been misspelt. Underline it then write the correct spelling on the line given.

Plural nouns usually end in 's'.

(b) Write **3** plural nouns from the text.

(i) ______________

(ii) ______________

(iii) ______________

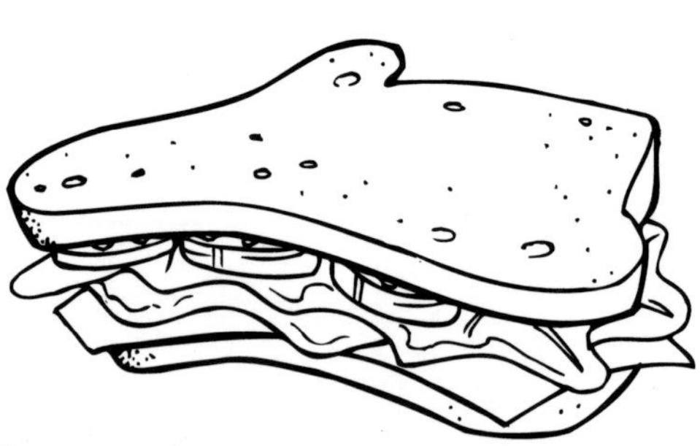

❸ *Grammar*

Command verbs are used in procedures. Command verbs tell you what to do.

(a) Write **4** command verbs from the text.

____

____

____

____

The missing clown

Editing skills

Read the newspaper report.

Police investigate missing clown

georgio, the ringmaster of the flying brothers' circus, reported today that a quantity of money had been stolen during the nite the mony, from the (sale/sail) of tickets, had been stored in the safe in the ringmaster's caravan

bozo the clown, who has also gone missing from the sircus, is wanted (by/buy) the police (to/too/two) help with their enquiries bozo did not appear (for/four) his usual segment in the show when his carivan was searched, his suitcase was gon and his costumes were left behind

polees investigations are continuing

❶ *Punctuation*

(a) Find **10** missing capital letters for the beginning of sentences and proper nouns. Write in **6** missing full stops.

❷ *Spelling*

(a) Circle the correct spelling where a choice of words is given.

(b) There are **6** misspelt words. Underline them then write the correct spelling above each word.

❸ *Grammar*

An apostrophe can show that something belongs to a person or thing. Who is the owner of these things? (The apostrophe is put after the owner or owners.)

(a) Write the owner or owners on the lines below.

(i) The ringmaster's caravan

____

(ii) The Flying Brothers' circus

____

Ned the elephant

Read the limerick.

(there/their) once was an elefant called ned

who wonted (to/too/two) sleep in a bed.

with the halp (off/of) his trunk

he climbed on thu top bunk

but found the pillow (too/to/two) small for his hed!

1 *Punctuation*

(a) Write **5** capital letters missing at the beginning of each line of the limerick and **1** capital for a proper noun. Circle **1** full stop and **1** exclamation mark.

2 *Spelling*

(a) Circle the correct spelling where a choice of words is given.

(b) There are **5** misspelt words. Underline them then write the correct spelling of the misspelt words.

____

____

____

____

____

3 *Grammar*

Common nouns name people, places and things. They do not have a capital letter.

(a) Write **6** common nouns from the limerick.

____

____

____

____

____

____

(b) Write **2** common nouns of your own.

____

____

PATTERNS AND RULES

N Number

1. Draw lines matching the pattern to the rule.

(a) 50, 52, 54, 56, 58, 60 •	• Counting forwards in odd numbers.
(b) 100, 99, 98, 97, 96, 95 •	• Counting backwards in fives.
(c) 11, 13, 15, 17, 19 •	• Counting forwards in even numbers.
(d) 50, 60, 70, 80, 90, 100 •	• Counting backwards in ones.
(e) 30, 25, 20, 15, 10, 5 •	• Counting forwards in tens.

2. Read the rule and continue the pattern.

(a) *Count backwards in tens* 100, 90, 80, ______ 10

(b) *Count forwards in threes* 3, 6, 9, ______ 39

(c) *Count backwards in threes* 42, 39, 36, ______ 0

(d) *Count in odd numbers* 71, 73, 75, ______ 99

(e) *Count backwards in even numbers* 20, 18, 16, ______ 2

CHALLENGE Write your own number pattern and the rule.

Pattern: ______

Rule: ______

______

Objective ***Counts in steps of 1, 2, 3, 5 and 10, forwards and backwards.***

MATCH THE NUMBER

N Number

1. Cut out the numbers below and glue each one on the correct picture.

(a) 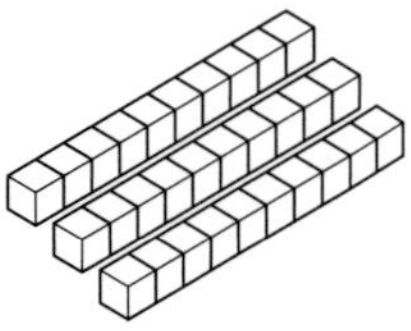		(b) 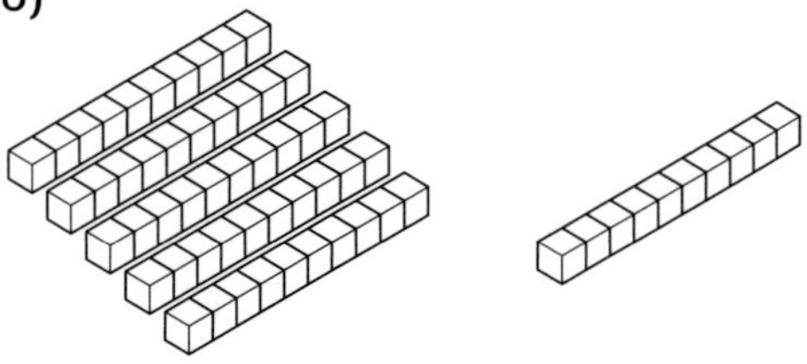	
(c) 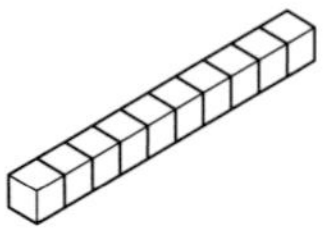		(d) 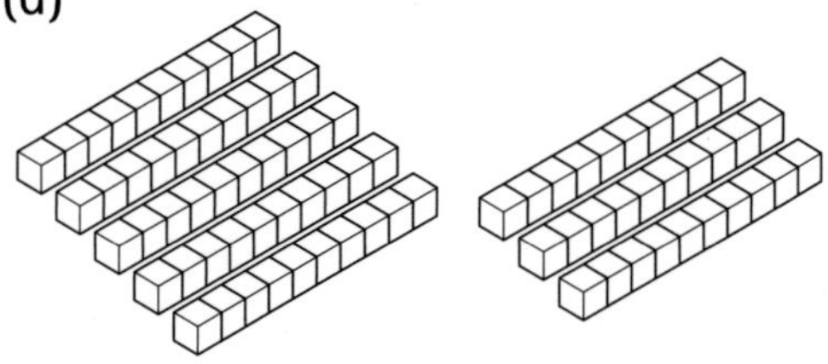	
(e) 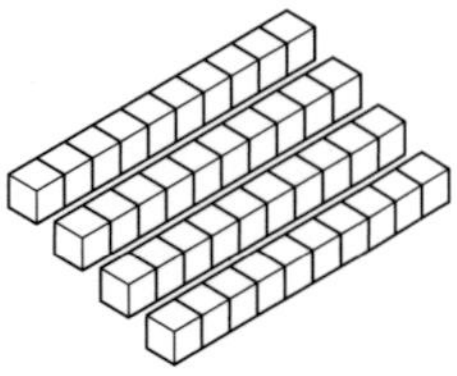		(f) 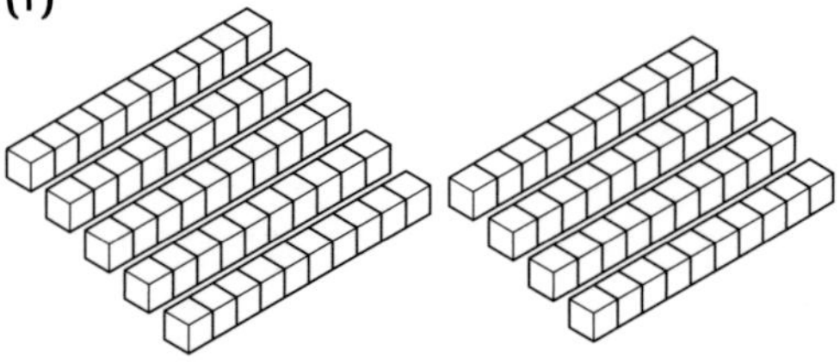	
(g) 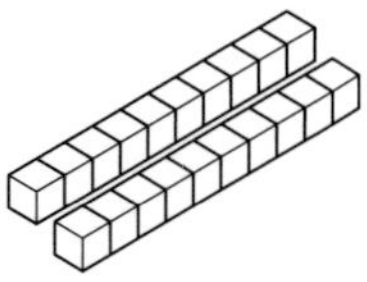		(h) 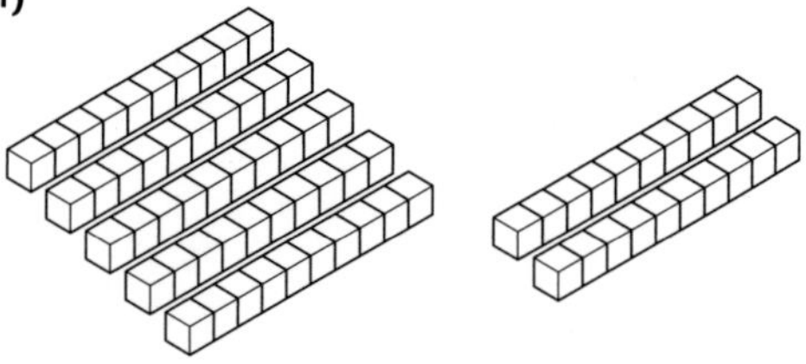	
(i) 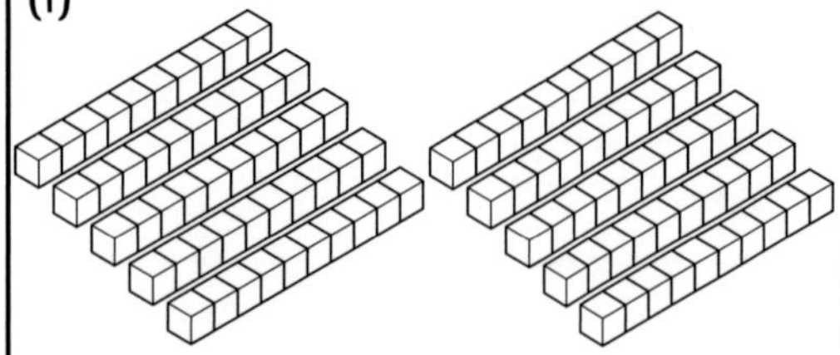		(j) 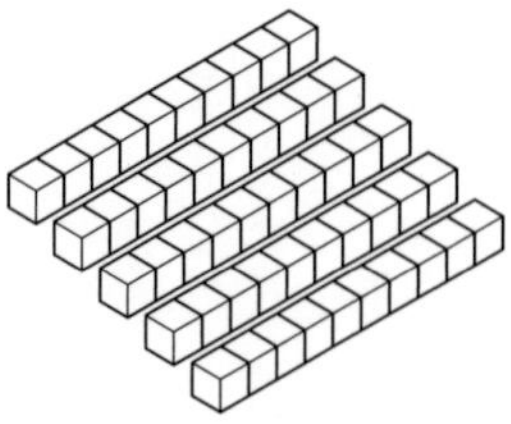	

10	20	30	40	50	60	70	80	90	100

CHALLENGE Make all of the numbers above, using the place value blocks.

Objective *Identifies numbers represented by place value blocks.*

ADDING

N Number

1. Write the number sentences for each picture.

(a) 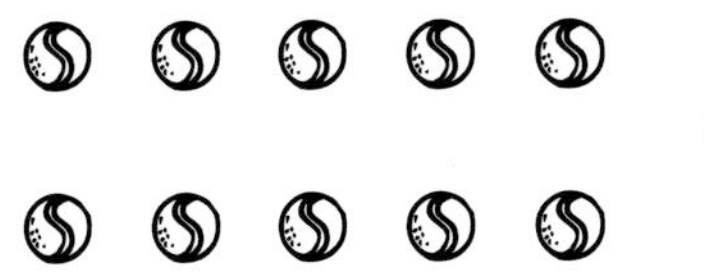	+	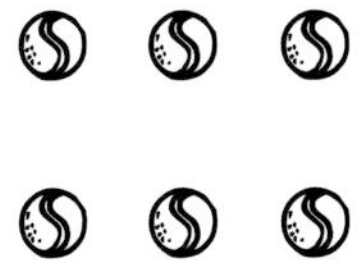	Number sentence _______ + _______ = _______
(b) 	+	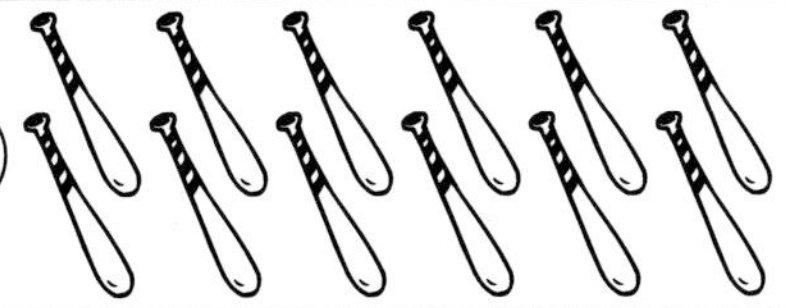	Number sentence _______ + _______ = _______
(c) 	+		Number sentence _______ + _______ = _______
(d) 	+		Number sentence _______ + _______ = _______
(e) 	+		Number sentence _______ + _______ = _______

2. Write the number sentence and add the place value blocks.

(a) 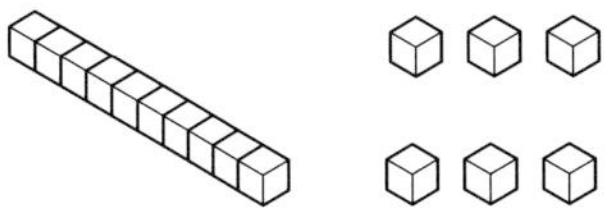	+		Number sentence _______ + _______ = _______
(b) 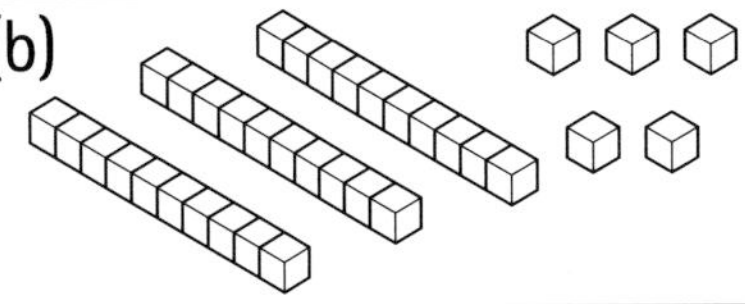	+		Number sentence _______ + _______ = _______
(c) 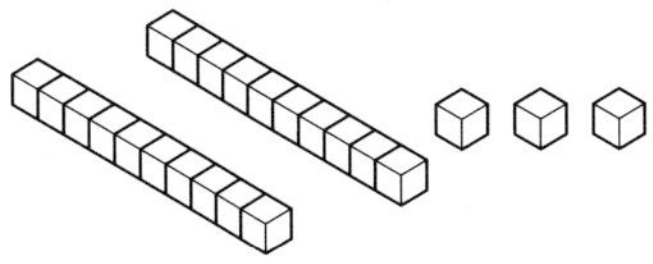	+	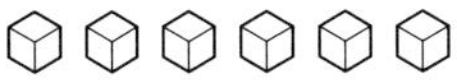	Number sentence _______ + _______ = _______

3. Fill in the answers on the grid.

+	15	19	10	11	18	12	17	14	16
5									

CHALLENGE

Add eight instead of five to each of the numbers above and record your answers.

____

Objective ***Adds a one-digit number to any two-digit number.***

METHODS OF SUBTRACTION

N Number

1. Use partitioning to solve these subtraction sums.

Example:	39 – 24	=	39	–	20	–	4
			19	–	4		
			15				

(a) 48 – 16 = ☐ – ☐ – ☐
= ☐ – ☐
= ☐

(b) 57 – 32 = ☐ – ☐ – ☐
= ☐ – ☐
= ☐

(c) 59 – 24 = ☐ – ☐ – ☐
= ☐ – ☐
= ☐

(d) 64 – 41 = ☐ – ☐ – ☐
= ☐ – ☐
= ☐

2. Use the expanded method to solve these subtraction sums.

Example: 39 – 24

	30	+	9		
–	20	+	4		
	10	+	5	=	15

(a) 47 – 12
☐ + ☐
– ☐ + ☐
☐ + ☐ = ☐

(b) 56 – 33
☐ + ☐
– ☐ + ☐
☐ + ☐ = ☐

(c) 65 – 44
☐ + ☐
– ☐ + ☐
☐ + ☐ = ☐

(d) 79 – 52
☐ + ☐
– ☐ + ☐
☐ + ☐ = ☐

(e) 88 – 27
☐ + ☐
– ☐ + ☐
☐ + ☐ = ☐

CHALLENGE

On the back of the sheet, solve these subtraction sums.

(a) 83 – 21 (b) 96 – 74 (c) 79 – 56

Objective ***Solves subtraction sums using partitioning and the expanded method.***

COMPARING MASS

1. Colour the heavier object in each pair.

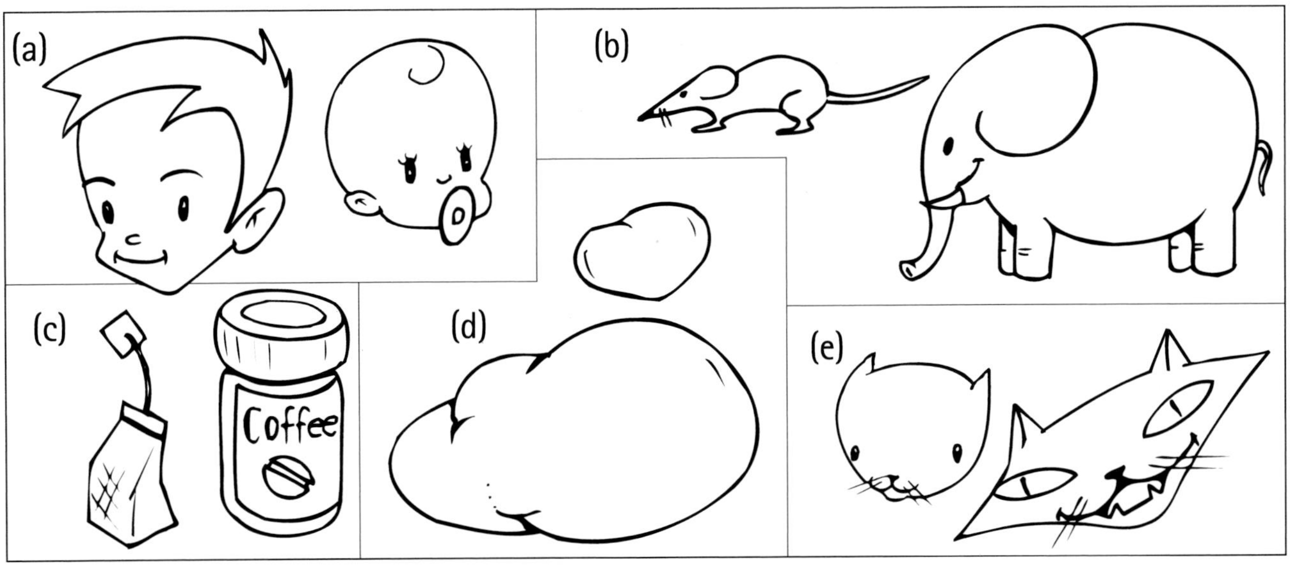

2. Write the symbols < less than, > more than, and = equal to.

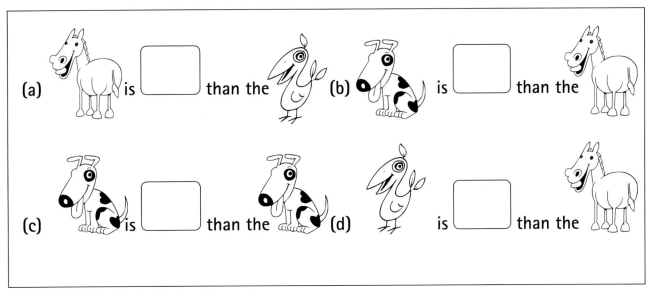

(a)  is ☐ than the 

(b)  is ☐ than the 

(c)  is ☐ than the 

(d)  is ☐ than the 

3. Write three things that are heavier than (>) your pencil.

(a) ____________ (b) ____________ (c) ____________

4. Write three things that are lighter than (<) your pencil.

(a) ____________ (b) ____________ (c) ____________

CHALLENGE

On the back of the sheet, write and draw three things in the classroom that have a greater mass than your pencil case.

Objective *Identifies the mass of everyday objects using symbols <, > and =.*

MEASUREMENT

1. Fill in the missing centimetres on this ruler.

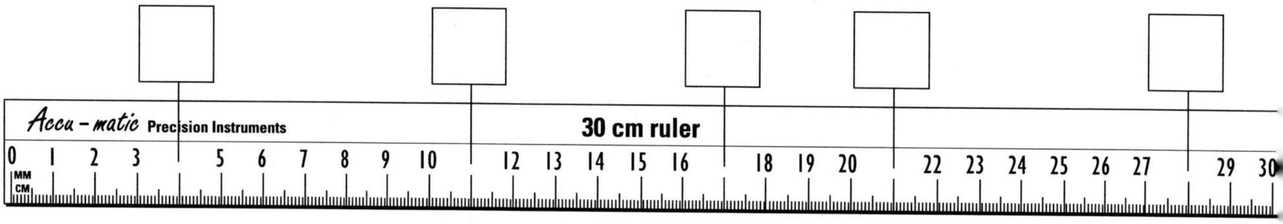

2. Fill in the missing numbers (counting by 10s) on the metre ruler.

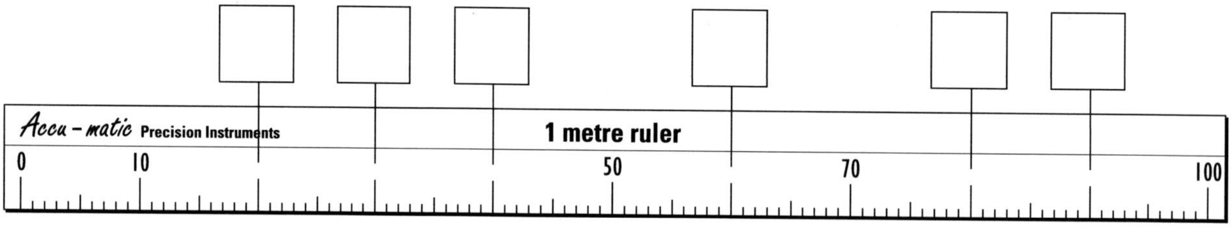

3. Write the weight shown on these kitchen scales.

(a)

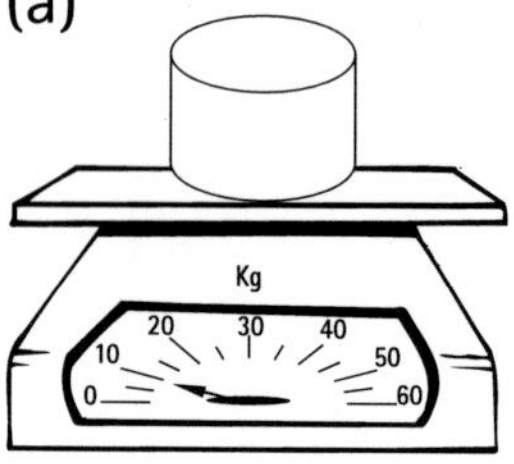

_________ kg

(b)

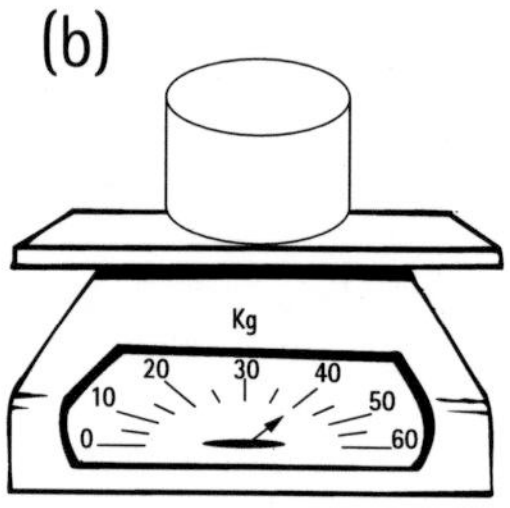

_________ kg

(c)

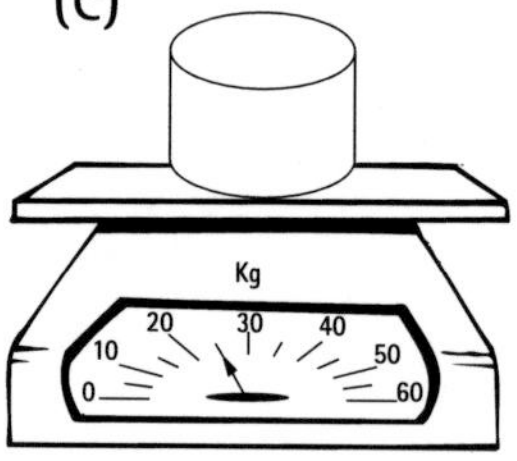

_________ kg

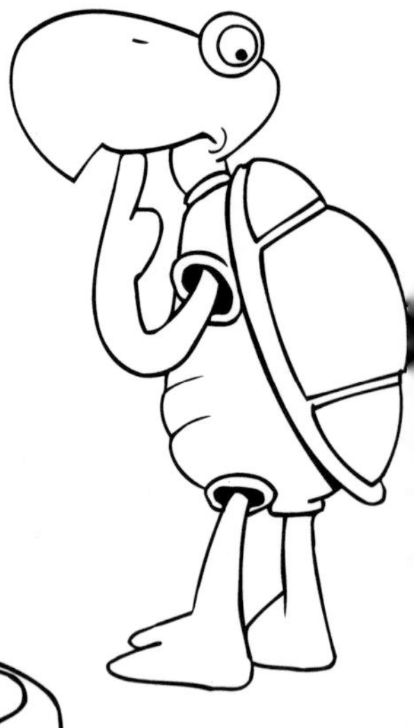

4. Write the capacity shown on these jugs of water.

(a)

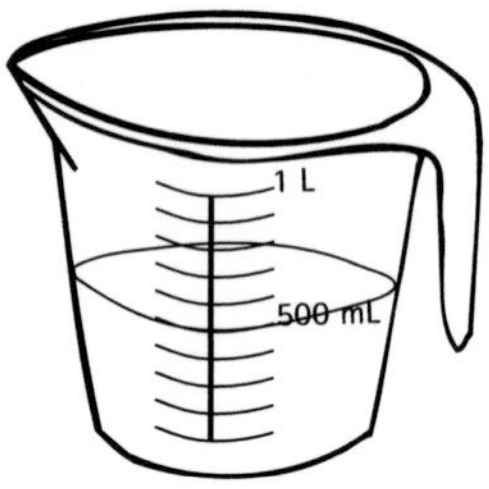

_________ mL

(b)

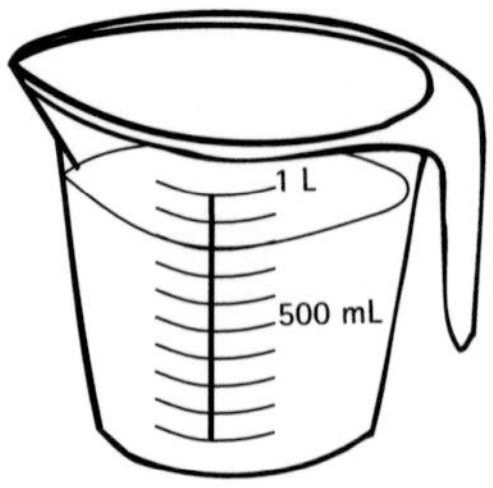

_________ mL

(c)

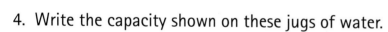

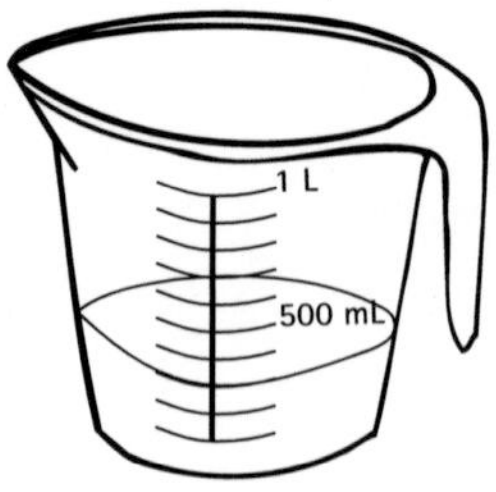

_________ mL

CHALLENGE

Measure the length of the following objects to the nearest centimetre.

(a) pencil = _________ cm (b) book = _________ cm (c) table = _________ cm

Objective *Reads scales to the nearest division.*

SHAPES IN PICTURES

1. Find and colour these shapes in the picture.

   triangles *(blue)*, **squares** *(red)*, **rectangles** *(green)*, **circles** *(yellow)*

2. Draw your own house using shapes.

CHALLENGE

On the back of the sheet, draw a rocket using shapes.

Objective ***Recognises and draws 2-D shapes in pictures.***

DESCRIBING 2-D SHAPES

1. Colour the shape that matches the description.

(a) Round, with no corners.	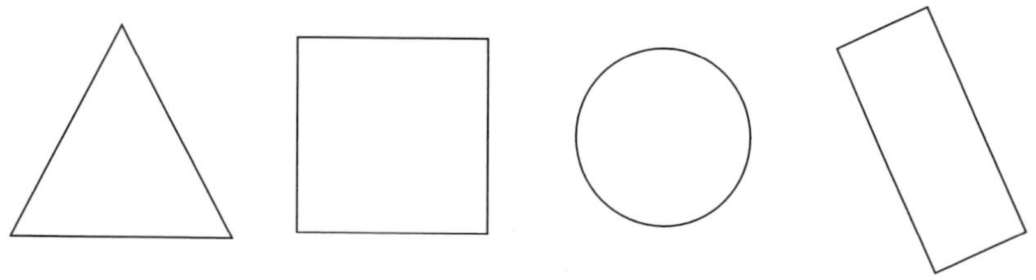
(b) Four equal sides and four corners.	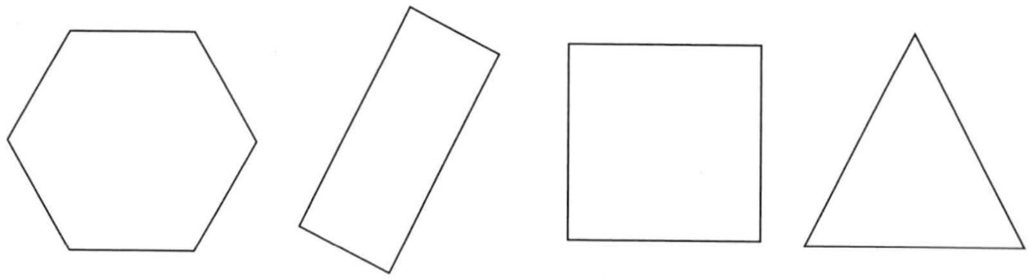
(c) Four sides (opposite sides equal) and four corners.	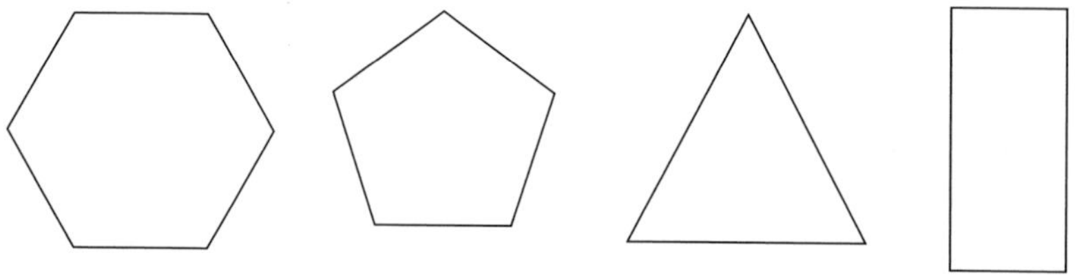
(d) Three equal corners and three sides.	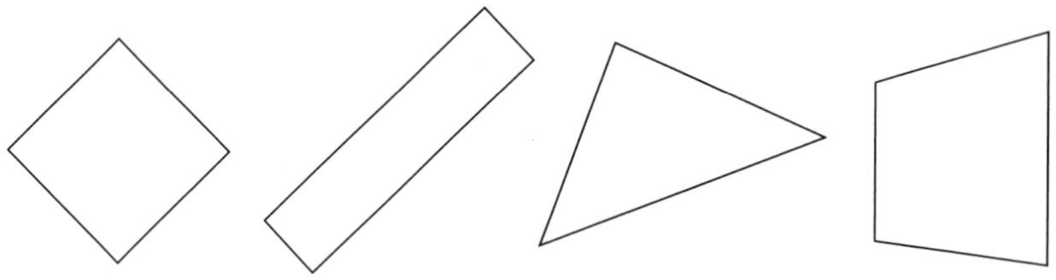

2. Look at the shape picture and fill in the description.

Sides:

(a) 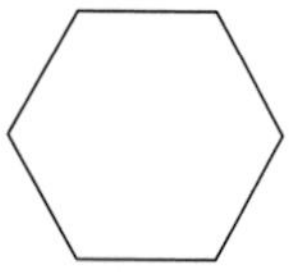 ______ sides. ______ corners. straight | curved

(b)  ______ sides. ______ corners. straight | curved

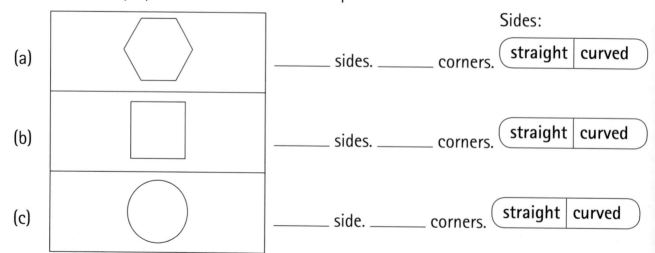

(c) 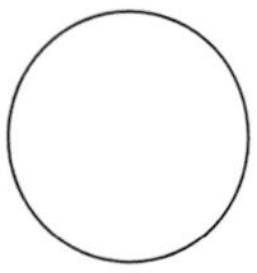 ______ side. ______ corners. straight | curved

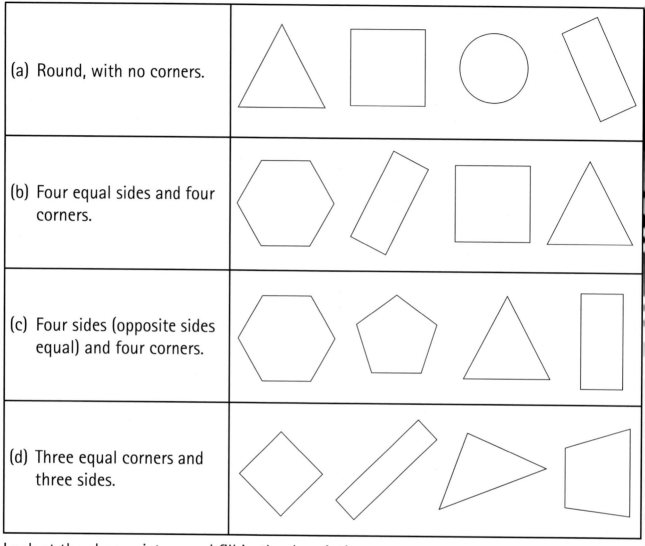

CHALLENGE

On the back of the sheet, draw and describe a cube. How many faces, edges and corners does it have?

Objective ***Describes features of 2–D shapes.***

My tree

1 Sit down near your tree and watch it for two minutes.
Write or draw three things that you see.

2 Sit very quietly and listen.
What do you hear near or in your tree?
Write or draw about two noises you can hear.

3 Look at the leaves of your tree. Pick up a leaf and trace it onto the back of this page. Write three words to describe your leaf.

Place another sheet of paper onto the bark. With the side of a crayon, make a rubbing. Cut out a piece of your rubbing and glue it here.

4 Touch the bark on your tree.
What does it feel like?
Write two words to describe it.

5 Draw your tree.

My environment

1 Look at the picture.

(a) Draw a green tick on four things that are natural.

(b) Draw a red cross on four things that have been built.

2 We share the environment with plants and animals.

What plants and animals can you see in the picture?

Plants	Animals and insects

Caring for my environment

1 Look at these children caring for each environment. Draw and write about another way you can care for these places.

I am putting things where they belong.

At school

I am tidying my room.

At home

I am recycling newspapers.

In the community

2 What would these places be like if we stopped caring?

WEEK 4

ENGLISH

Comprehension – The Mermaid of Zennor 81–83
Comprehension – Whuppity Stoorie 84–86
Grammar – Adverbs 87–88
Writing – Report, Penguins 89–91
Editing Skills – Caterpillars to Butterflies 92
Editing Skills – The Lion and the Mouse 93
Editing Skills – How a Letter Reaches its Destination 94

MATHEMATICS

Number – Tens and Ones 95
Number – How Many Tens and Ones? 96
Number – Subtracting 97
Number – More Subtraction 98
Measurement – The Litre (L) 99
Measurement – Capacity 100
Geometry – Symmetrical Shapes 101
Geometry – Symmetry 102

SCIENCE

Myself – About Me 103
Myself – Changes 104
Myself – A Need or a Want? 105

The Mermaid of Zennor – 1

Text

Read the legend.

Long ago, in the village of Zennor, there lived a handsome young man with a beautiful voice. His name was Matthew Trewhella. Every Sunday evening, when he sang in church, everyone loved listening to his voice. They said he had the voice of an angel.

One spring Sunday evening, while Matthew was singing, a beautiful young woman dressed in fine clothes slipped silently into a pew at the back of the church. After the singing finished, she slipped just as silently away. Every Sunday evening, the young woman returned to the village church. She stayed to hear Matthew sing, and then crept away.

One evening, while Matthew was singing, another voice joined Matthew's as he sang. The two voices filled the church with such sweet music that everyone was astonished. Finally, Matthew turned to see who was singing. When his eyes met those of the young woman, he became instantly entranced. When the singing ended, the young woman left the church. Matthew quickly followed. Eventually, by the banks of a stream, the two met. The villagers, realising that the two had formed a special bond, left them alone and went home.

The following morning, the villagers were alarmed to discover that Matthew had not returned home. They carefully searched the bogs and woods, but no trace of Matthew was found.

One day in spring, the following year, a fisherman came to the Trewhella family to give them news. He told how he had been fishing off Pendour Cove when a mermaid called to him. She asked him politely if he could move his anchor because it was blocking the entrance to the cave. In the cave her baby and beloved Matthew were waiting for her. After moving his boat, the fisherman hurried back to the harbour at Zennor. He was eager to share with Matthew's family what he had learnt about Matthew's fate.

Although Matthew was greatly missed by all, everyone was pleased to know he was so happy.

Sometimes, in the evening, the villagers believe they can still hear two glorious voices floating along with the sound of the wind and waves.

My learning log	When I read this legend, I could read:		
	_________ all of it.	_________ most of it.	_________ some of it.

The Mermaid of Zennor – 2

Comprehension

1. What event changed Matthew's life?

___

2. Using words and phrases from the text, describe Matthew's singing.

___

3. What word means:

   (a) a long bench in a church? p___

   (b) filled with wonder and delight? e___

   (c) feelings that join people? b___

   (d) frightened, scared? a___

4. Which phrase or words begin this legend? ___

5. Why weren't the villagers worried when they saw Matthew talking to the young woman after church?

___

___

6. Why didn't Matthew notice the young woman when she first came to the church?

___

___

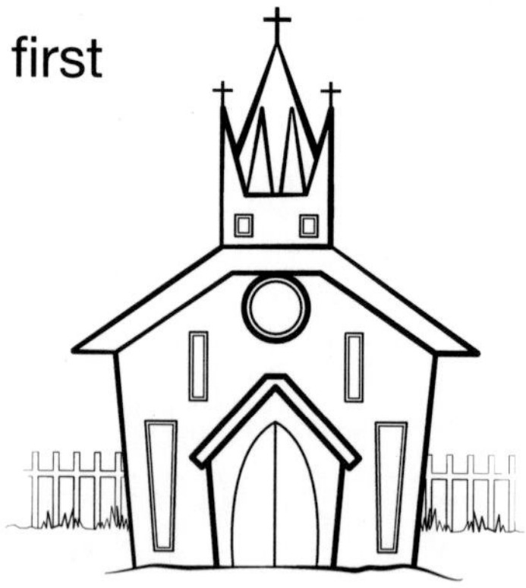

7. Using information in the text, and other information you know, describe mermaids.

___

___

___

8. Matthew and the mermaid probably lived ___

___.

My learning log	While doing these activities:		
	I found Q ___ easy.	I found Q ___ tricky.	I found Q ___ fun.

The Mermaid of Zennor – 3

Word Reading

1. Which word from the text is a homophone for each word below?

   (a) here ______________________ (b) mist ______________________

   (c) sea ______________________ (d) fete ______________________

   (e) bean ______________________ (f) no ______________________

2. Circle the correct homophone in each sentence.

   (a) Kazim had a **not** / **knot** in his laces.

   (b) Do you **know** / **no** the man in the green cap?

   (c) Mum was **sew** / **so** happy to **see** / **sea** her son.

3. (a) Write the word missing from this part of the sentence.

   … another voice joined Matthew's ____________ as he sang.

   (b) The apostrophe shows that Matthew owns the ____________.

4. (a) What sound does the letter 'c' make in the word 'voice'? ____________

   (b) Underline the two words with the same sound.

church	**clothes**	**such**	**trace**
crept	**entrance**	**music**	**cave**

5. The verb 'hurry' has been changed to 'hurried' by changing the 'y' to 'i' and adding the suffix '-ed'.

   Write a new verb for 'hurry' by adding the suffix '-es'.

   ____

My learning log	Write **Yes** or **No**. I know which homophone to use. ____________ I can recognise the soft 'c' sound. ____________ I know to change the 'y' to 'i' before adding suffixes. ____________

Whuppity Stoorie – 1

Read the fairy tale written as a poem.

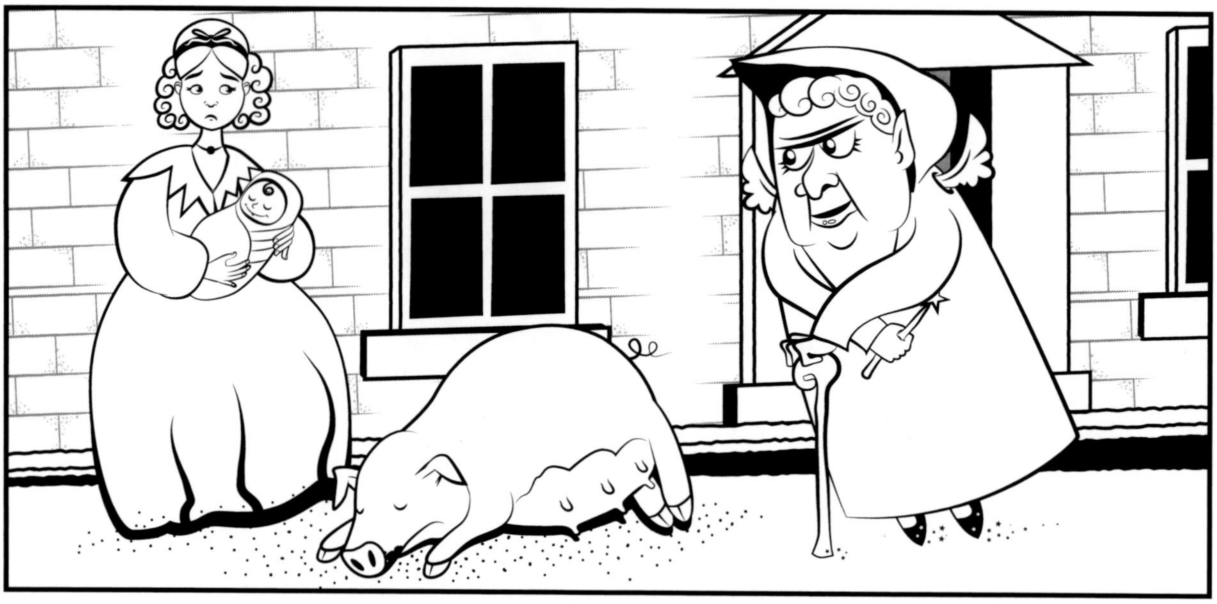

Once upon a time, there was a woman whose husband went to a fair.
Sadly he never returned and the woman had a baby in her care.
Her only possession was a chubby sow that was close to dying.
The widow was very worried then a fairy woman heard her crying.

'I'll heal your sow', the fairy said, 'if you can guess my name.
But if you don't, in three short days, your baby is mine to claim!'
The widow thought all night about what the name could be.
On the second day, in the forest, what a sight she happened to see!

In a quarry, the fairy woman sat spinning and singing cheerfully,
'Whuppity Stoorie is my name. Whuppity Stoorie! That's me!
In one more day, I'll ask my question and claim my precious prize.
The widow will never guess my name no matter how hard she tries.'

The fairy arrived to question the widow. 'Take me instead,
Although I'm not worthy to tie the laces of Whuppity Stoorie!' she said.
Whuppity Stoorie went, screeching away, and no-one ever found her.
But the widow and her baby, as best they could, lived happily ever after.

My learning log	When I read this poem, I could read:		
	________ all of it.	________ most of it.	________ parts of it.

Whuppity Stoorie – 2

Comprehension

1. A possession is ______________________________.

2. A widow is ______________________________.

3. A sow is ______________________________.

4. Which phrases begin and end a fairy tale like this one?

____

____

5. Why do you think the sow was chubby?

____

6. If you could ask Whuppity Stoorie a question, what would it be?

____

7. Which event solved the widow's problem?

____

____

8. Which sad event changed the widow's life?

____

9. What would have happened if the sow had not got sick?

____

____

10. What happened to the baby?

____

11. (a) Copy an interesting word or phrase from the text.

____

(b) Why did you choose it? ______________________________

My learning log	While doing these activities:		
	I found Q ______ easy.	I found Q ______ tricky.	I found Q ______ fun.

Whuppity Stoorie – 3

1. (a) What sound does the letter 'a' say after 'qu' in 'quarry'? ____________

   (b) Underline the two words with the same sound.

quad	quack	quail	quality	quake

2. (a) Which two words have the same sound after 'w' as 'worthy'? Underline them.

window	worm	world	widow	what	whose

   (b) Write a sentence using both of these words.

   ____

3. How many syllables in each word?

   (a) Whuppity ____________

   (b) precious ____________

   (c) possession ____________

   (d) cheerfully ____________

4. (a) Write the two smaller words that make up each contraction.

   I'll ____________ don't ____________

   that's ____________ I'm ____________

   (b) What does an apostrophe do in a contraction? ____________

5. Write each verb before the suffix was added.

   (a) tries ____________ (b) dying ____________

   (c) spinning ____________ (d) screeching ____________

   (e) cheerfully ____________ (f) lived ____________

   (g) worried ____________ (h) happily ____________

My learning log	Write **Yes** or **No**. I can recognise the 'or' sound after a 'w'. ____________ I am able to count syllables in words. ____________ I know the two words that make up contractions. ____________

How things happen

1. (a) Read the sentences.

Jill walked slowly up the steep hill.

'Wait for me', Jack yelled loudly.

'You'll have to run fast and catch up', Jill said.

At the top of the hill, they carefully filled their pail with water.

On the way down, Jack fell over and hurt his head badly.

'How sad, too bad', said Jill sweetly.

Then, she ran off happily, without poor old Jack!

(b) ***How*** did these things happen?

(i) Jill walked.

(ii) Jack yelled.

(iii) They filled the pail.

(iv) Jack was hurt.

(v) Jill said, 'How sad, too bad'.

(vi) Jill ran off.

Words telling how things happen are called *adverbs*.

2. Write the *adverb* that tells how you should do these things.

(a) cross the road ______________ safely/dangerously

(b) work in groups in the classroom ______________ loudly/quietly

(c) smile ______________ sadly/happily

(d) do your school work ______________ carefully/carelessly

(e) run in a race ______________ slowly/quickly

Adverbs

The elephant park

***Yesterday**, we went to an elephant park. There were elephants **everywhere**. Trainers were **gently** washing the elephants in the river.*

***Soon**, the elephant show began. The elephants moved **gracefully** and some of them played a game of football. One elephant took a man's hat off his head and then **carefully** put it back.*

***Finally**, four elephants painted pictures. They painted flowers and trees. **Later**, we bought one of the paintings to take home.*

*I've **always** wanted to ride an elephant—and guess what? I did and it was great!*

Words that tell how, when and where things happen are called *adverbs*.

1. Answer each question with an adverb.

(a) When did they go to the elephant park? ____________________

(b) Where were there elephants? ____________________

(c) How were the trainers washing their elephants? ____________________

(d) When did the show begin? ____________________

(e) How did the elephants move? ____________________

(f) How did the elephant put the hat back? ____________________

2. Write *how*, *when* or *where* after each adverb.

(a) gracefully ______________ (b) carefully ______________

(c) yesterday ______________ (d) soon ______________

(e) everywhere ______________ (f) later ______________

Penguins

Penguins are members of the bird family.

Although they are birds, penguins cannot fly. They spend most of their time in water and can swim very well.

Their wings are like flippers and help them to swim. Their body is shaped like a torpedo. This helps them to move smoothly through the water.

Penguins have short, thick, shiny feathers. Their feathers are darker on their back and lighter on their belly. Enemies such as seals cannot see them as easily in the water.

Penguins eat fish, squid and krill, which are like tiny prawns. A hook at the end of their bill helps them to grab their food.

I like the way penguins move in the water. It looks as if they are flying. When they are on land, they move with a funny waddle.

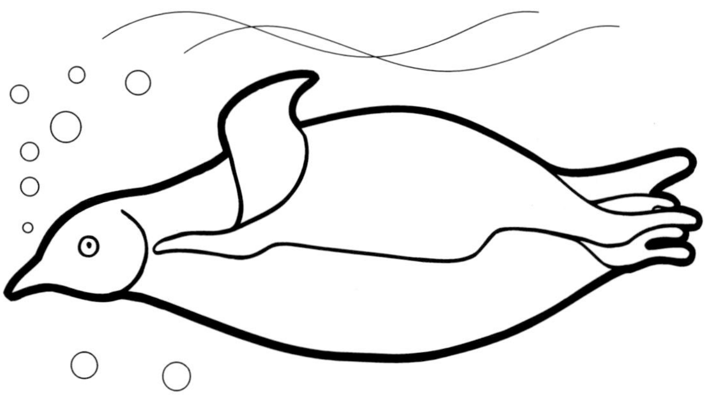

Use the report on page 39 to complete the page.

1. Title

2. Classification

What are they?

3. Description

What do they look like?

Where do you find them? ______________________________

What can they do? ______________________________

____

____

____

4. Conclusion

Finish the sentences about the ending.

(a) Penguins look as if they are ______________________ in the water.

(b) When penguins are on ______________________, they move with a ______________________ waddle.

 978-1-912760-62-6 www.prim-ed.com Prim-Ed Publishing

1. Plan a report about an animal.

Title

Classification

What is it?

Description

Draw or write words about what it looks like.

Where do you find it?

What can it do?

Conclusion

What do you think about it?

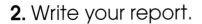

2. Write your report.

3. Check your work.

Caterpillars to butterflies

Read the explanation.

Editing skills

this is how caterpillars tern into butterflies ________________

a female buterfly lays eggs on a green leaf ________________

after about ten days tiney caterpillars hatch ________________

they begin to look for food the catarpillars grow ________________

and grow as they continue to eat when thay ________________

are fully grown, eatch caterpillar changes into a ________________

chrysalis arfter about two weeks, ________________

out cum colourful butterflies ________________

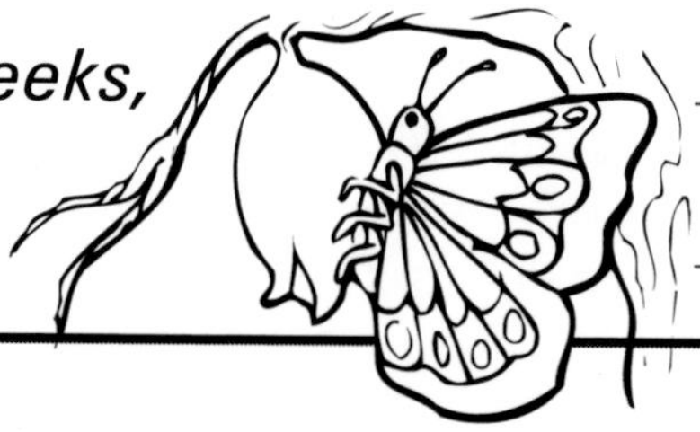

❶ *Punctuation*

(a) Find **7** missing capital letters and **7** full stops.

❷ *Spelling*

(a) One word in each line has been misspelt. Underline it then write the correct spelling on the line given.

One way a noun can be made plural is by adding 's'; for example, ' book – books'.

(b) Write the plural of each word.

(i) egg ________________

(ii) day ________________

(iii) caterpillar ________________

(iv) week ________________

❸ *Grammar*

Adjectives are words which describe nouns.

(a) Write adjectives from the text that describe these nouns.

(i) ________________ butterfly

(ii) ________________ leaf

(iii) ________________ butterflies

(iv) ________________ caterpillars

(b) Write **2** adjectives of your own for this noun: *eggs*

____

____

The lion and the mouse

Editing skills

Read the fable.

a big lion wos asleep in the jungle he woke up __________

when a mouse ran ova him the lion was angry __________

he caught the little mowse and opened his __________

mowth to eat him the mouse was very scared __________

'please let me go! im only littel but one day I __________

may be able to halp you' __________

the line decided to let him go one day, the lion __________

was caught in a trap maid of rope the mouse __________

saw the lion he nibbled at the rops and set __________

him fwee __________

Moral: Even small friends are worth having.

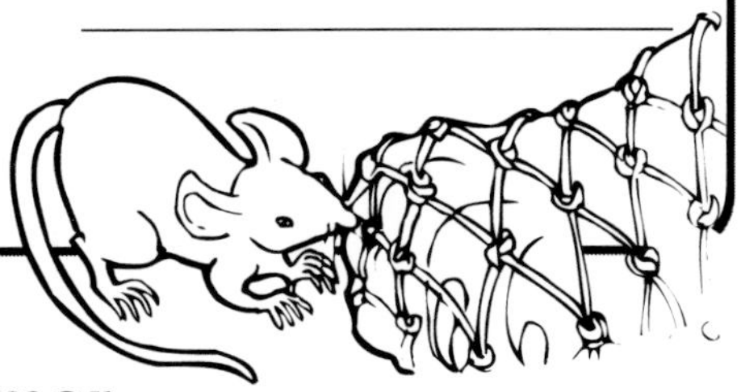

❶ *Punctuation*

(a) Find **11** missing capital letters and **10** full stops. Circle **1** exclamation mark. An apostrophe is needed in **1** word where letters have been left out.

(b) Draw a line under the actual words the mouse says and circle the speech marks.

❷ *Spelling*

(a) One word in each line has been misspelt. Underline it then write the correct spelling on the line.

❸ *Grammar*

Joining words can join different ideas in a sentence. They can also make a longer sentence by joining two or more shorter ones. Some joining words are 'and', 'so', 'when' and 'but'.

(a) Circle then write **2** joining words used in the text.

____

____

How a letter reaches its destination

Editing skills

Read the explanation.

after a letta is posted, a postal van collects the __________

(male/mail) and tackes it to the post office __________

(There/Their) it is sorted bi size and __________

(where/wear) it is to go some will go by truk __________

and some by (plain/plane) or trane when it __________

reaches its destination, another postel worker __________

leaves it at the post ofice (for/four) you to __________

colect or delivers it (to/too/two) your letterbox __________

❶ *Punctuation*

(a) Find **4** missing capital letters and **4** full stops.

(b) Circle **2** commas in the text.

❷ *Spelling*

(a) Circle the correct spelling where a choice of words is given.

(b) One word in each line has been misspelt. Underline it then write the correct spelling on the line given.

❸ *Grammar*

(a) Write the two smaller words which make up these words.

(i) another

__________ __________

(ii) letterbox

__________ __________

(b) Write the nouns used in the text to name **3** different types of transport used to take mail to its destination.

__________ __________

____

TENS AND ONES

1. Look at the pictures of the blocks and fill in the numbers.

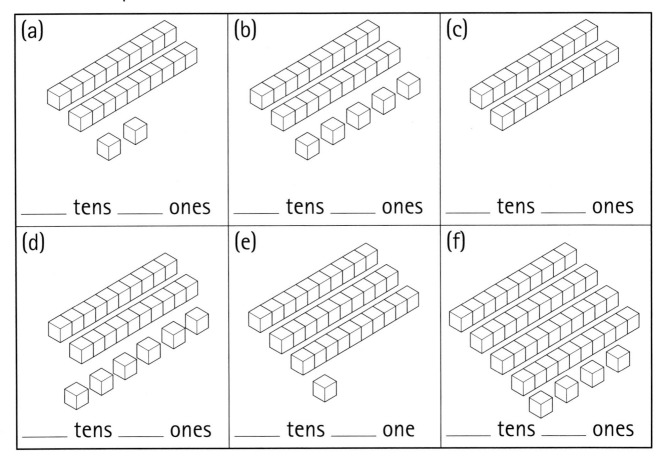

(a)

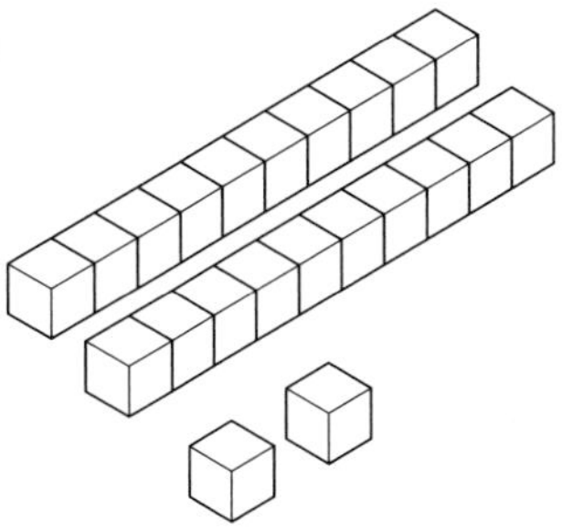

_____ tens _____ ones

(b)

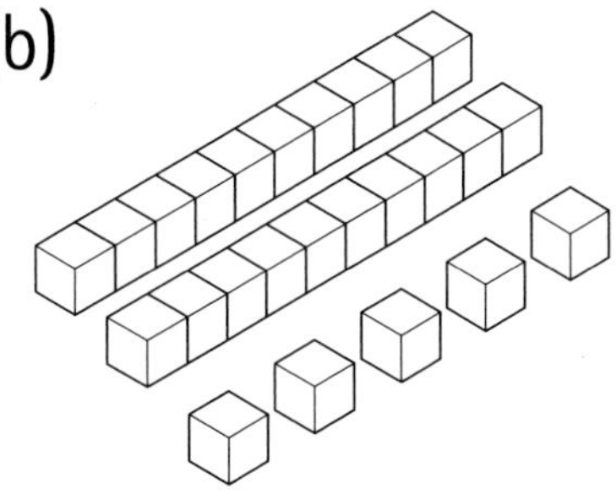

_____ tens _____ ones

(c)

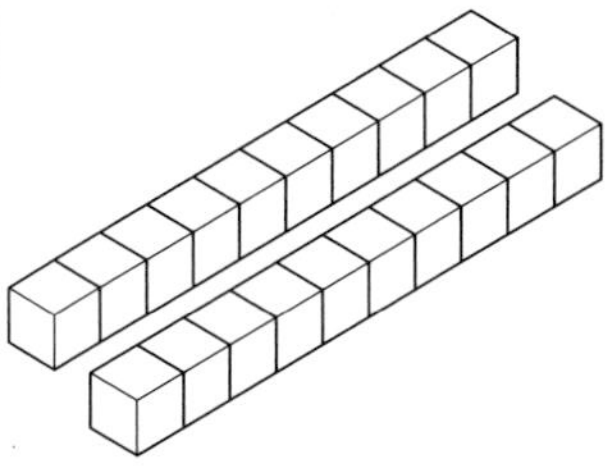

_____ tens _____ ones

(d)

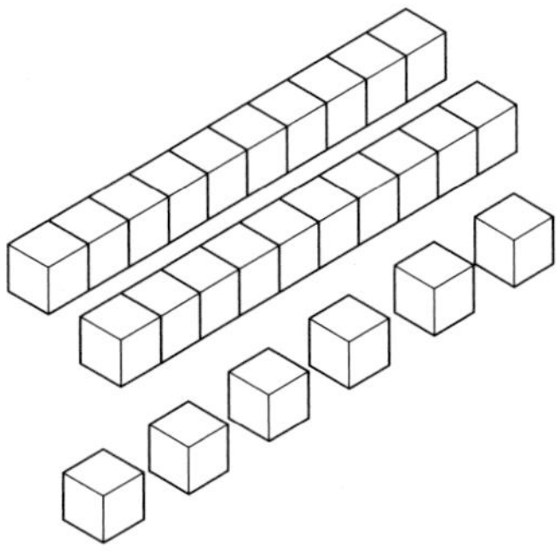

_____ tens _____ ones

(e)

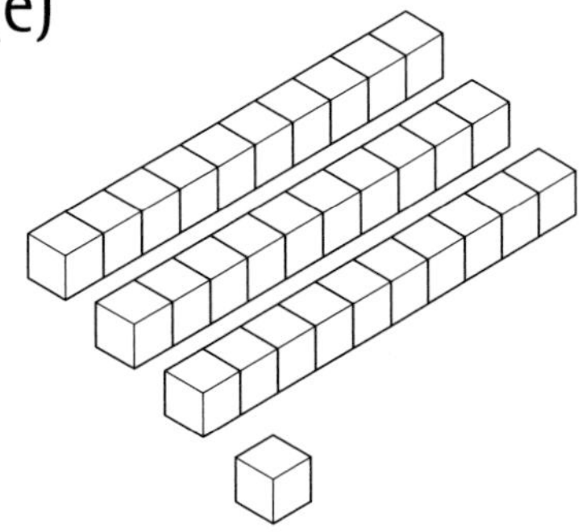

_____ tens _____ one

(f)

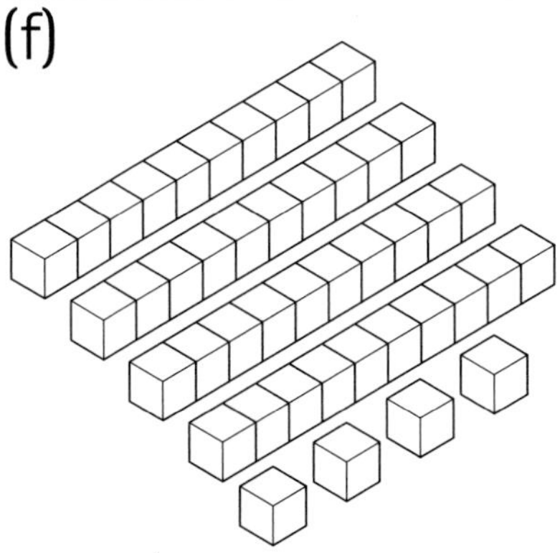

_____ tens _____ ones

2. Colour the blocks to match the number.

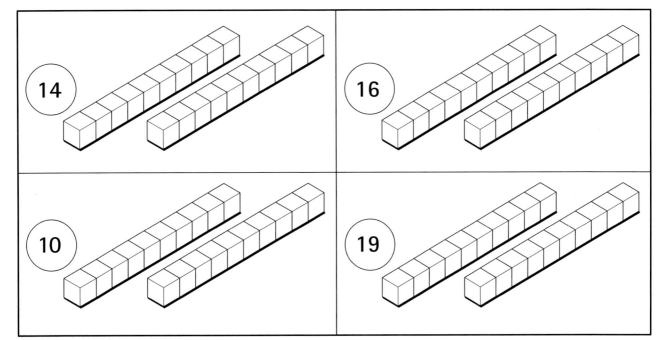

14

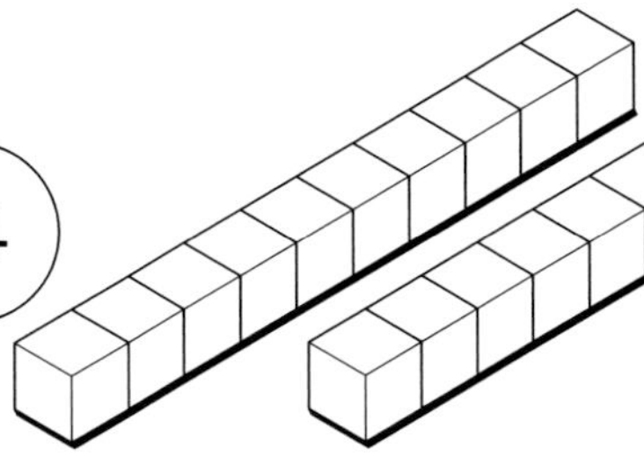

16

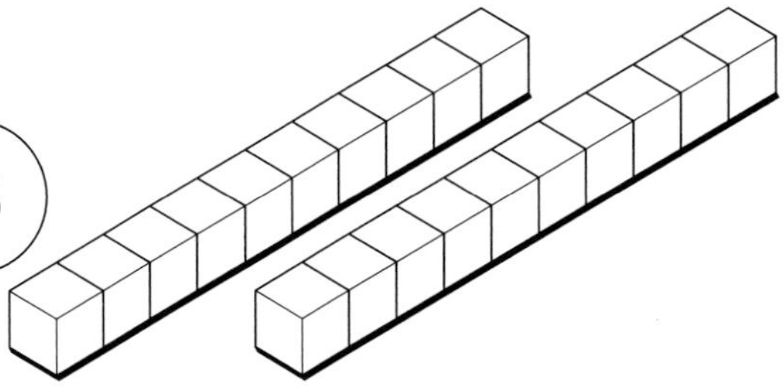

10

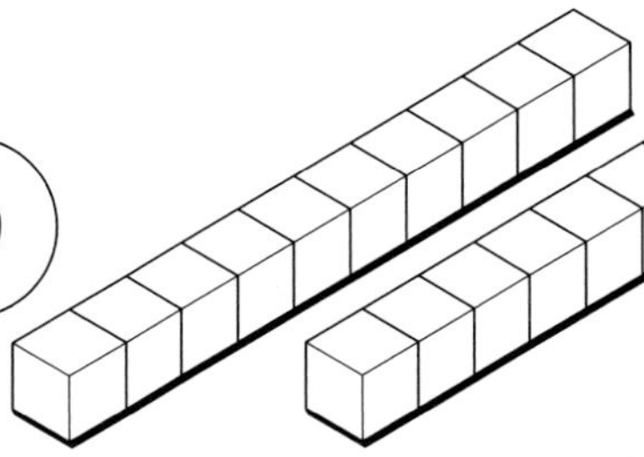

19

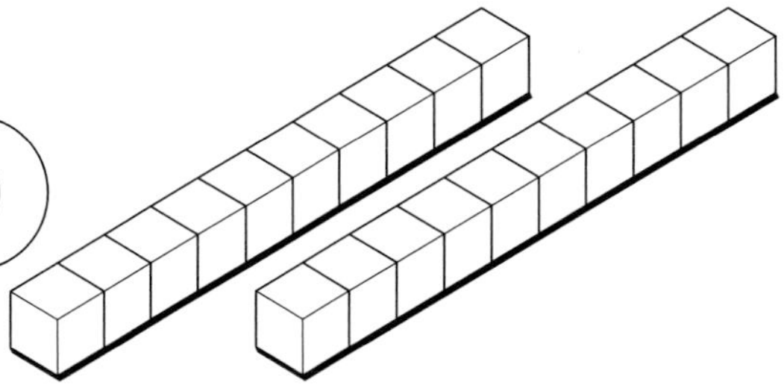

CHALLENGE Using the tens and ones blocks, make these numbers – 12, 17, 19, 27 and 29.

Objective ***Identifies what each digit in a two-digit number represents.***

HOW MANY TENS AND ONES?

N Number

1. Count how many tens and ones, then write the number.

Note:  = 10  = 1

(a) 	☐ ten ☐ ones = ☐
(b) 	☐ tens ☐ one = ☐
(c) 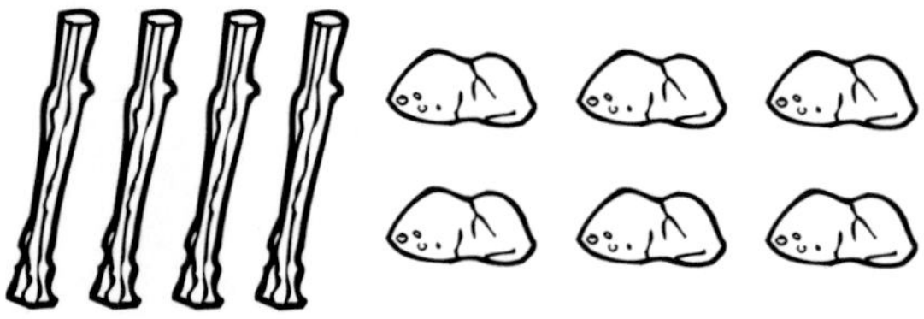	☐ tens ☐ ones = ☐
(d) 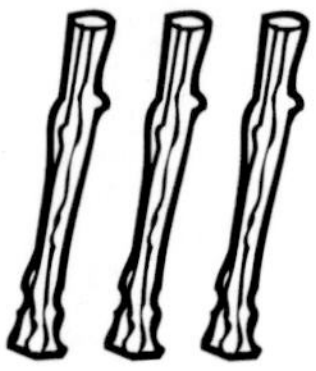	☐ tens ☐ ones = ☐
(e) 	☐ tens ☐ ones = ☐

2. Draw these numbers using sticks and stones.

(a) 15 = 1 ten and 5 ones	
(b) 27 = 2 tens and 7 ones	
(c) 19 = 1 ten and 9 ones	

CHALLENGE

On the back of this sheet, draw these numbers, using pictures of sticks and stones: 38, 45 and 72.

Objective ***Identifies what each digit in a two-digit number represents.***

SUBTRACTING

N Number

1. Write the number sentence for each picture.

(a) 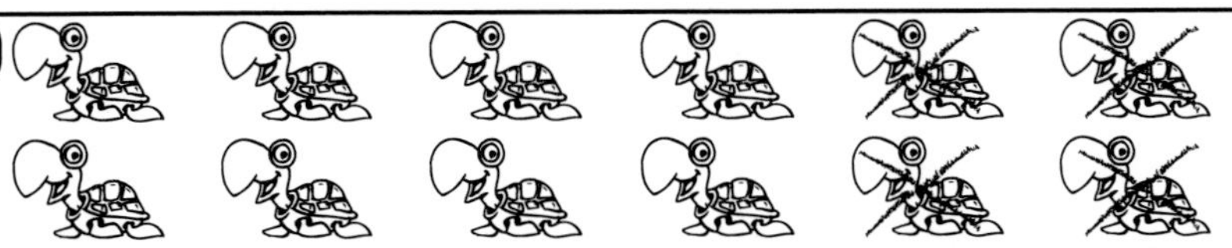	Number sentence _____ – _____ = _____
(b) 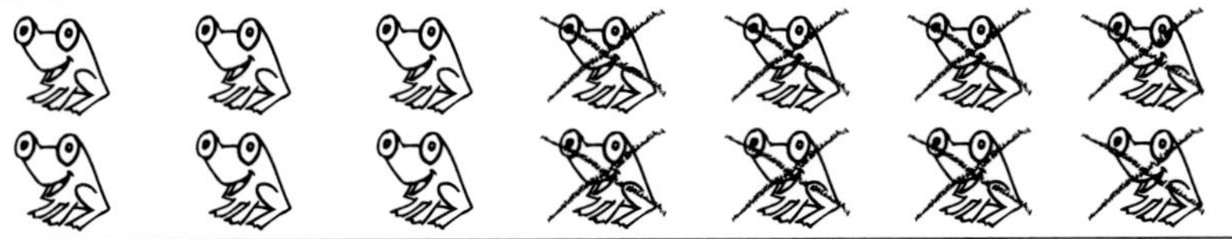	Number sentence _____ – _____ = _____
(c) 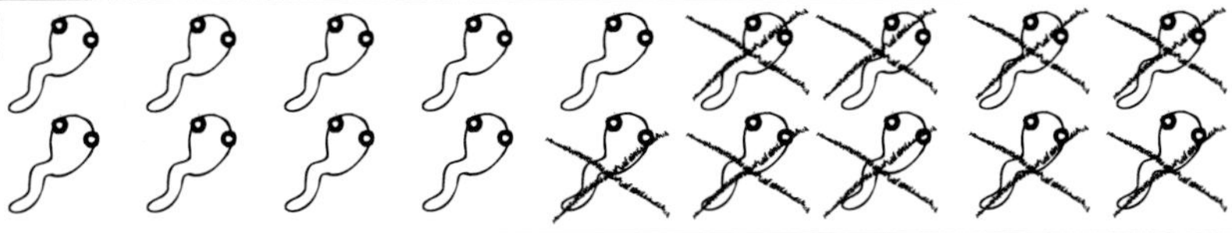	Number sentence _____ – _____ = _____
(d) 	Number sentence _____ – _____ = _____
(e) 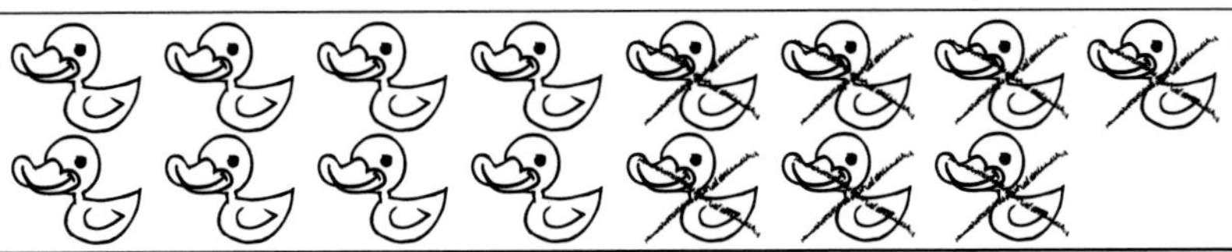	Number sentence _____ – _____ = _____

2. Subtract the place value blocks and write the number sentence.

(a) 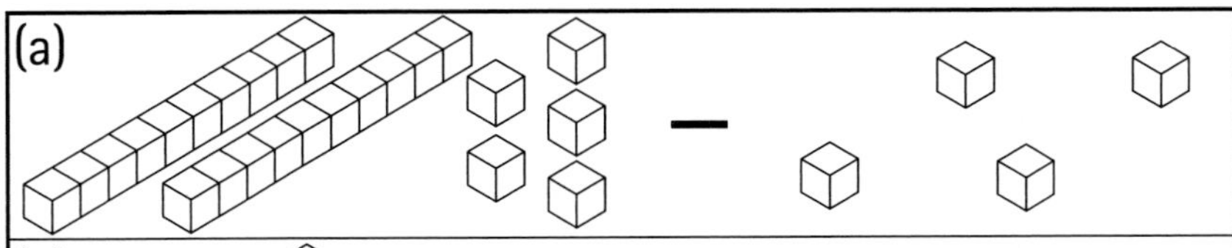	Number sentence _____ – _____ = _____
(b) 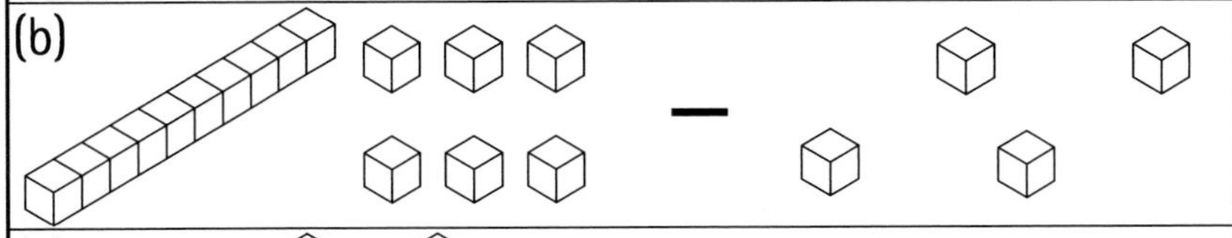	Number sentence _____ – _____ = _____
(c) 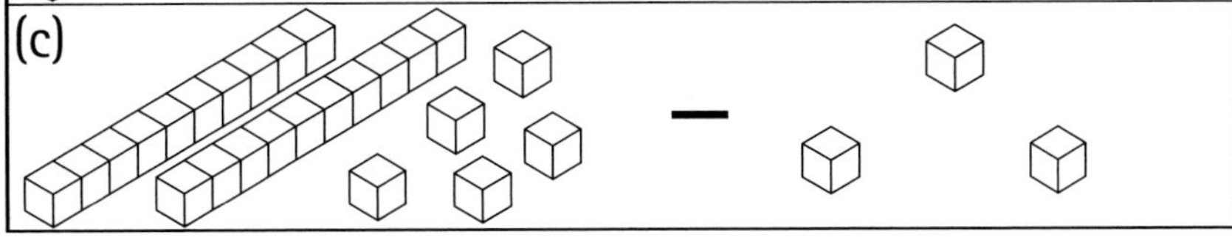	Number sentence _____ – _____ = _____

3. Fill in the answers on the grid.

–	10	13	12	19	15	11	17	14	20
5									

CHALLENGE

Subtract 8 from each of the numbers above and record your answers.

____

Objective ***Subtracts a one-digit number from any two-digit number.***

MORE SUBTRACTION

N Number

1. Use the number line to help you solve these subtraction problems. Remember to start at the first number!

0 1 2 3 4 5 6 7 8 9 10 11 12 13 14 15 16 17 18 19 20

(a) 14 – 5 = ☐ (b) 20 – 3 = ☐ (c) 18 – 9 = ☐ (d) 17 – 10 = ☐

(e) 19 – 4 = ☐ (f) 13 – 7 = ☐ (g) 20 – 5 = ☐ (h) 16 – 8 = ☐

2. Draw lines to represent the subtraction problem. Show the answer by crossing off the lines.

(a) 20 – 4 = ☐	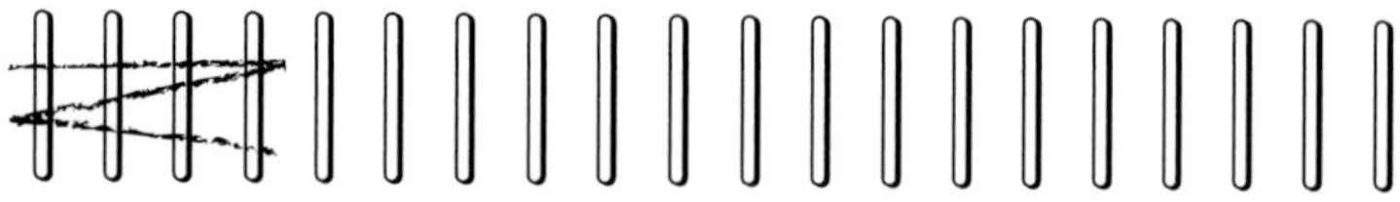
(b) 18 – 5 = ☐	
(c) 19 – 10 = ☐	
(d) 20 – 7 = ☐	
(e) 17 – 8 = ☐	

CHALLENGE

On the back of this sheet, draw and answer this subtraction problem. 'There were 20 tomatoes on the bush but the birds ate 6. How many are left?'

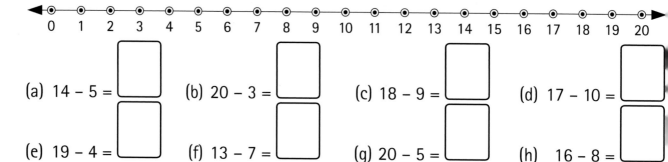

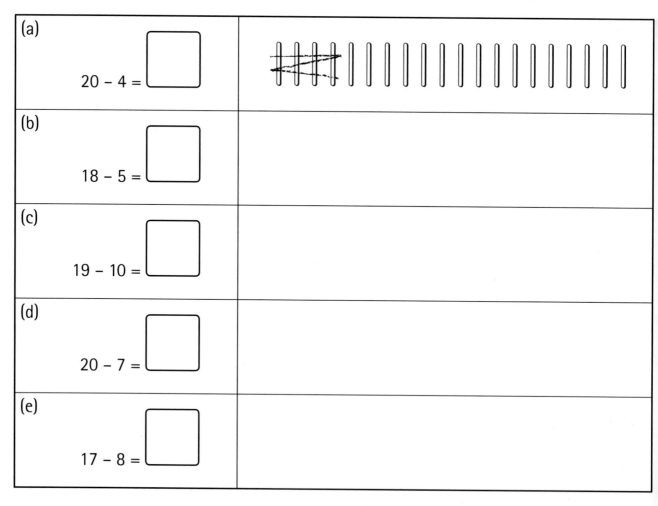

Objective ***Solves subtraction problems to 20.***

 978-1-912760-62-6 www.prim-ed.com Prim-Ed Publishing

THE LITRE (L)

1. How many cups of water does it take to fill a one-litre container?

Estimate: ☐ cups Measure: ☐ cups

2. Colour the containers that hold less than one litre red.
Colour the containers that hold more than one litre blue.

3. Estimate and measure how many litres of water it takes to fill the following.

(a) a bucket 	Estimate ☐ litres	Measure ☐ litres
(b) a rubbish bin 	Estimate ☐ litres	Measure ☐ litres
(c) an ice-cream container 	Estimate ☐ litres	Measure ☐ litres
(d) a plastic cup 	Estimate ☐ litres	Measure ☐ litres

CHALLENGE

Find and list three containers that hold one litre of water.

______________ ______________ ______________

Objective ***Estimates and measures capacity using litres.***

CAPACITY

Capacity means how much an object can hold.

1. Colour the objects with the larger capacity in each pair.

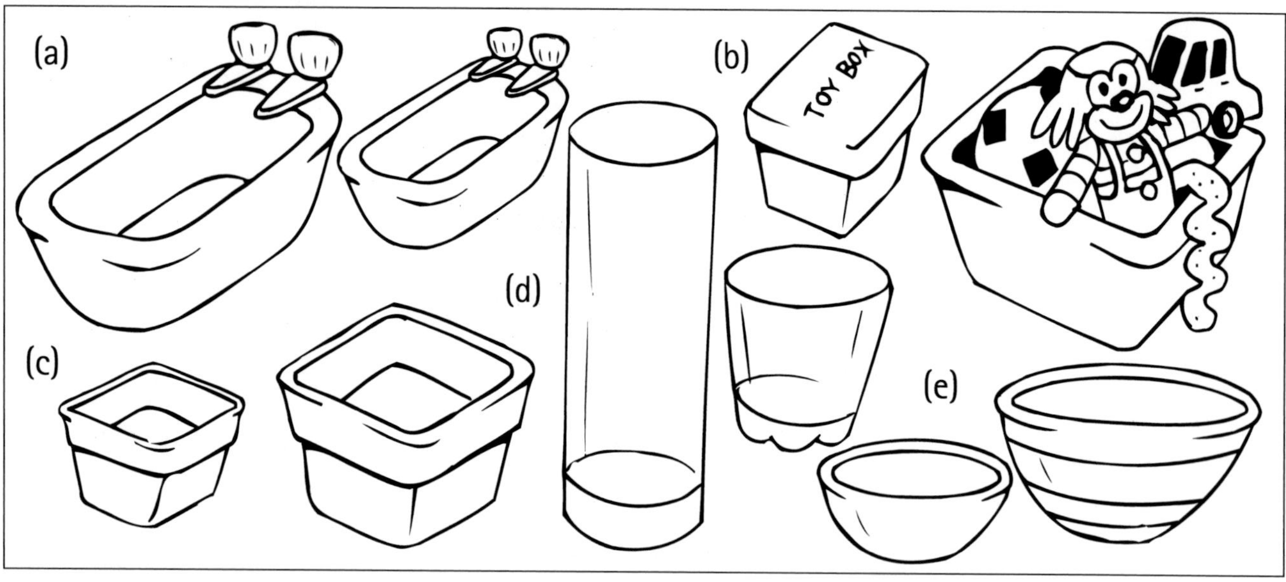

2. Write the symbols < less than, > more than, and = equal to.
The capacity of the ...

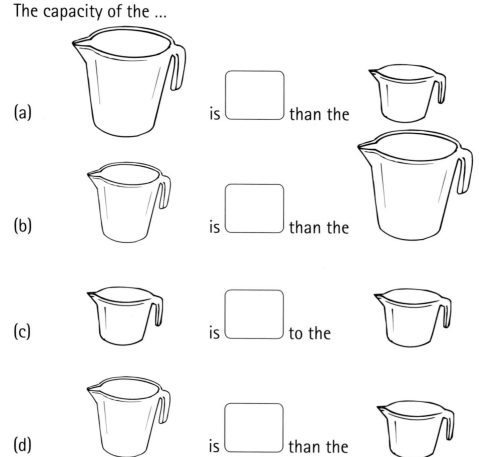

(a)  is ☐ than the 

(b)  is ☐ than the 

(c)  is ☐ to the 

(d)  is ☐ than the 

CHALLENGE On the back of the sheet, draw and label containers that are:
(a) full (b) empty (c) half-full

Objective *Identifies the capacity of everyday objects using appropriate vocabulary and symbols <, > and =.*

SYMMETRICAL SHAPES

1. (a) Cut out these shapes.

   (b) Fold each shape in half, to see if the two sides match.

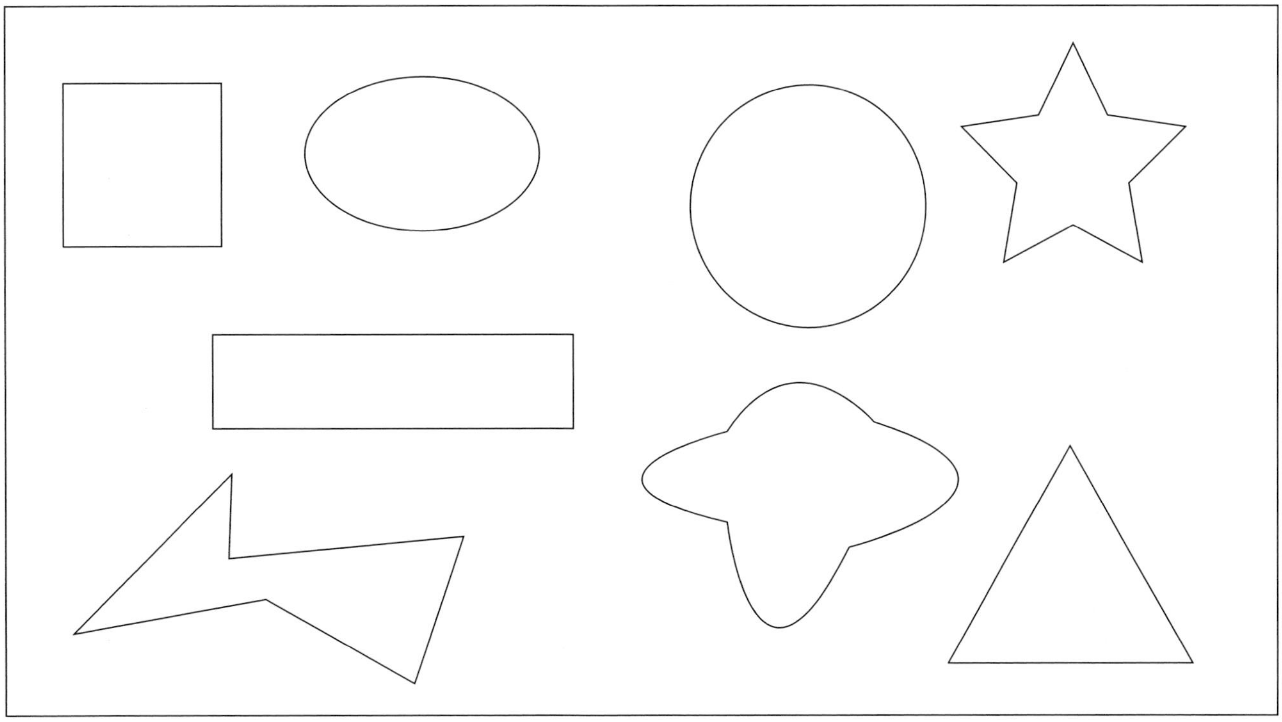

2. Choose two shapes that are symmetrical.

   Glue one shape into each box.

CHALLENGE

Glue a leaf onto a sheet of paper. Draw your own leaf next to it. Draw a line of symmetry on both leaves.

Objective ***Folds shapes in half and identifies symmetry.***

SYMMETRY

A symmetrical shape can be divided into half equally.

1. Draw the line of symmetry through these shapes.

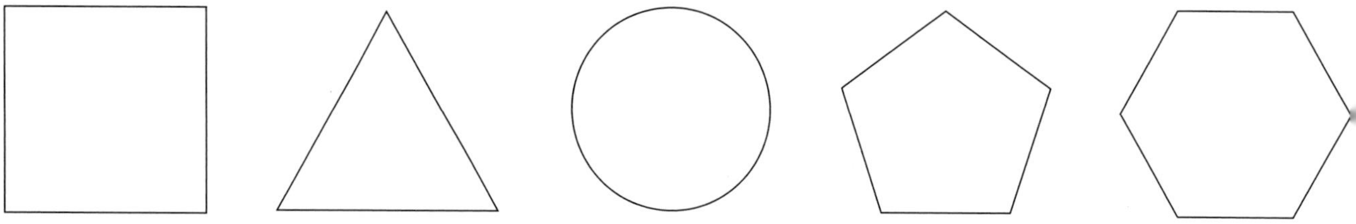

2. Draw the line of symmetry through these pictures.

(a)

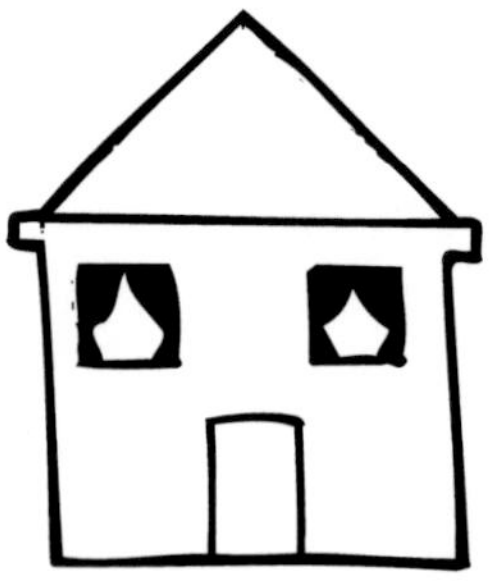

(b)

(c)

(d)

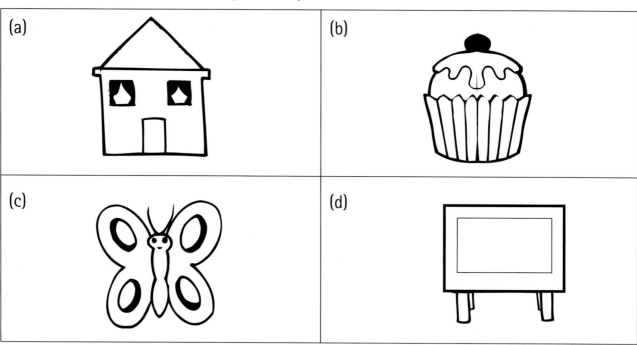

3. Complete these pictures to make them symmetrical.

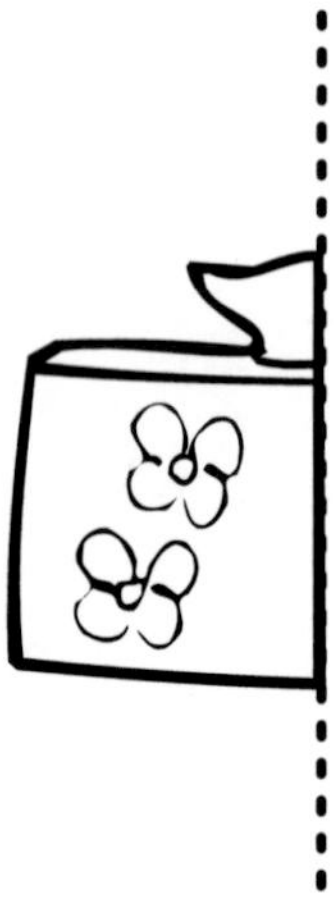

CHALLENGE

On the back of the sheet, draw half of a butterfly and ask a friend to draw the other half. Is the butterfly symmetrical?

Objective ***Identifies lines of symmetry and completes symmetrical pictures.***

About me

1 (a) Draw what you think you will look like as an elderly person.

(b) Draw a line to match the body parts to your drawing.

head	neck
nose	eyes
mouth	shoulder
arm	hand
knee	leg
ankle	foot

2 Draw or write something you can …

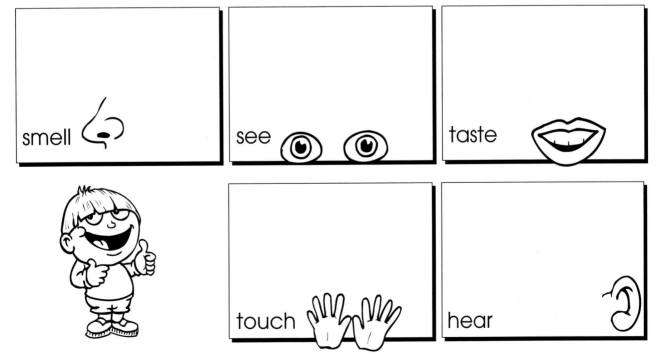

smell 

see 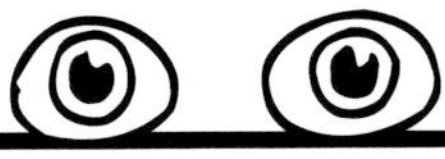

taste 

touch 

hear 

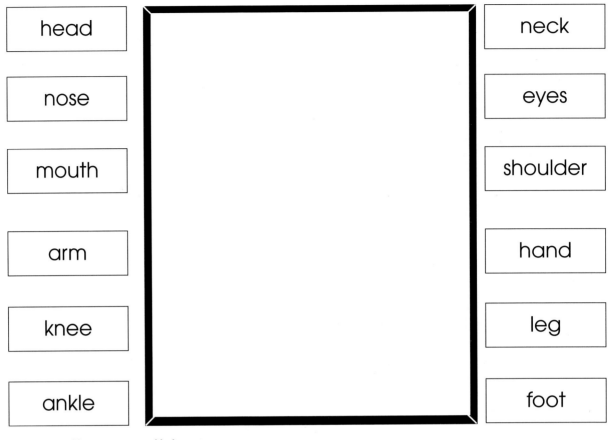

3 Which sense helps us to detect if something is hot and may burn us?

Changes

As we grow, many changes will happen to us.

1 Complete the table.

Stage	Like to do	Like to eat	Responsibilities
Baby			
Toddler			
Now			

2 Complete the missing parts of the human stages of life.

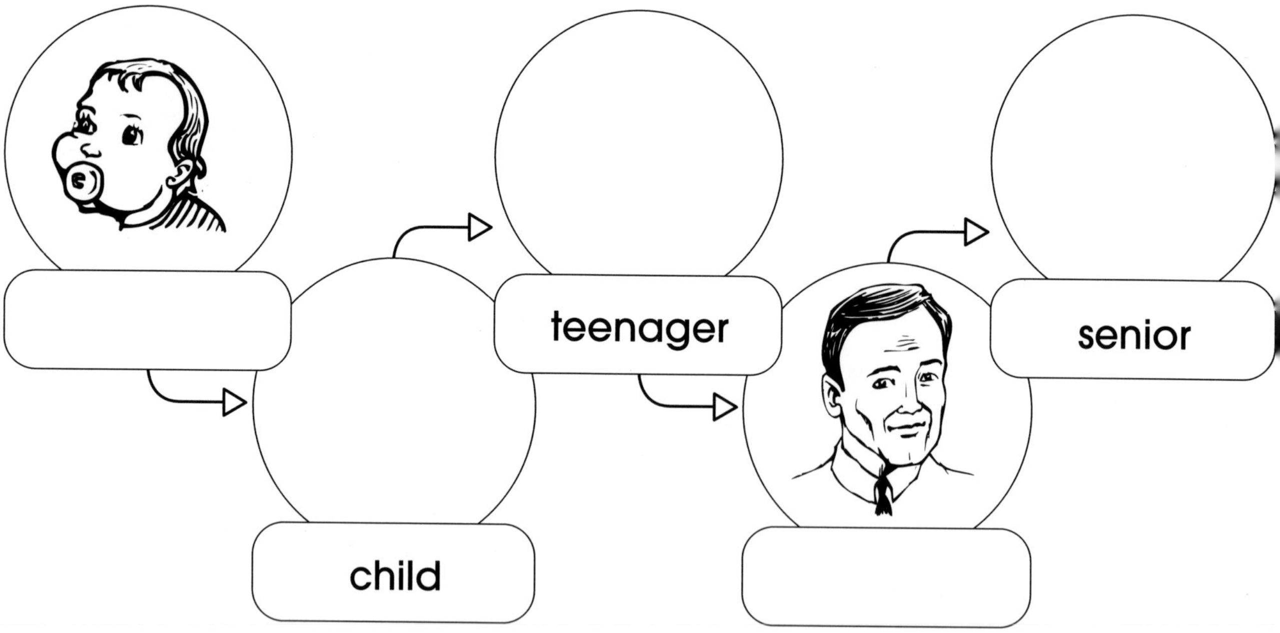

3 All living things grow and change. Match the plants and animals.

(a) kitten •	• frog
(b) seed •	• cat
(c) tadpole •	• butterfly
(d) caterpillar •	• plant

A need or a want?

**Foods and drinks are needed for people to live and grow.
Some foods and drinks are needs and others are wants.**

1. List four things you have had to drink in the last two days. Tick if you think the drink is a need or a want.

Drink	Need	Want

2. List six things you have had to eat in the last two days. Tick if you think the food is a need or a want.

Food	Need	Want

3. (a) How important to us are the drinks and foods we need?

Not important
Important
Very important

(b) How important to us are the drinks and foods that we want?

Not important
Important
Very important

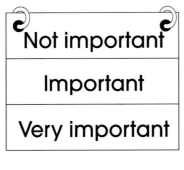